Raising Llamas

The Ultimate Guide to Llama Keeping and Caring, Including Tips on How to Raise Alpacas

Contents

Introduction

Did you learn about the advantages of raising a llama from a friend, the internet or somewhere else? Are you considering starting a farm? And do you want to enjoy all the benefits of having llamas – or their close cousins, alpacas?

Great! However, you may not know how to go about it and you likely have several questions you want answered.

What are the differences between alpacas and llamas? Can you raise them together? What should you have in place to start a farm? How do you go about buying a llama? What should you know to raise them properly?

This book answers those questions and more.

Or your case might be a little different. You might have raised one or two llamas on your own and then you got stuck. Well, don't fret. It's never too late to improve.

This book will help you learn how to raise llamas, including all the details about their care, behavior, breeds and much more.

We provide all the practical day-to-day information you need to know about llamas and alpacas. Our goal is to ensure that you have all you require in your quest to raising healthy llamas for any purpose, whether for fun or for a business venture.

You might have read other books that promised to give you all the information you need to know but under-delivered. So, you are wondering, what makes this book different? Don't worry! We will tell you.

This book is easy to read, with no scientific terms or facts that are hard to understand. You will also receive the latest information on the correct practices, and since we are experts, all the instructions and methods in this book can be used, have been used, and are still in use.

So, what are you waiting for?

It is time to get all that knowledge about llamas and alpacas you have been yearning for!

Chapter 1: Why Raise Llamas?

Quick Fact – *Llamas were domesticated and used as pack animals in the Peruvian highlands around 4000 to 5000 years ago.*

You may have come across a llama at some point, maybe in your neighborhood or at the local zoo. Their cute looks and hairy body might have drawn you to take a closer look at them.

But suddenly, they were chasing you and spitting at you! What memory will this experience leave you? It's likely you wouldn't want to go anywhere near them again!

Well, believe it or not, llamas are friendly and mild animals that make great pets. Previous mishandling from strangers and intruders might cause their sometimes-strange reactions, but when you keep one, you will discover they are lovely animals to have.

Llamas and their closely-related cousins, alpacas, are one of the oldest domestic animals known to man. They both belong to the camel family and are popular as pack animals. Though similar, they can be differentiated by their size and hair.

Llamas are part of the camelid family, a family that first appeared about 40 million years ago on the Central Plains of North America. It was only about 3 million years ago that the llamas' ancestors migrated to South America. Around 10,000 to 12,000 years ago, the last Ice

Age caused the camelid's to become extinct in North America. Now, in Canada and the United States, there are about 100,000 alpacas and 160,000 llamas. And, as a fun fact, it may interest you to know that the national symbol of Peru is the llama, and it can be found on the flags, stamps, coins and other tourist products in Peru.

For farm and ranch owners, llamas and alpacas are an excellent fit for a mixed farming system. They are ruminant animals with three stomach compartments and like cattle and sheep, they also chew their cud. For folks with a small piece of land, you can care for one or two llamas, and although big, they are relatively easy to care for.

If you are a homesteader looking to add a new animal to your livestock herd, then llamas will be a great fit. For folks who need a new pet at home, llamas are popular because of their friendly nature. Now, let's talk about the benefits of raising llamas.

8 Major Reasons Why You Should Raise a Llama

1. Protection

It is common for livestock like goats, sheep, horses and cows to be hunted by predators. This problem has become a common threat to herders who look for various means to keep predators away. A pack of coyotes is enough to take down big livestock like cows and horses, but you can reduce the risk of attacks from predators by introducing llamas into your herd.

Research by Iowa State University shows that, on average, farmers lose 11 percent of their herd to predators, but this is reduced to 1% when llamas are introduced into the herd. Most farmers introduce llamas into their herd to guard other livestock, mostly using gelded males for this purpose.

They have proven to be an excellent substitute for dogs, requiring less care. One llama is enough to guard hundreds of other animals. Incorporating a llama into your herd is relatively easy because of their quick adaptation. Although some might adapt within hours, others might need 1 or 2 weeks to adapt to other animals completely.

After adapting to other animals, they will chase predators away from the farm. Llamas have good instincts with full awareness of their surroundings and usually draw attention to a stranger (predator) by raising an alarm call. This sound is then followed by chasing, kicking, or spitting at the intruding animal.

2. They are great pack animals

How about enjoying an outdoor adventure with a llama carrying all the burden? Sounds great, right?

Llamas have been raised and used as pack animals for thousands of years. They might not be as popular for this purpose as horses and oxen, but they get the job done. Their history traces back to South America, where the animal used to carry loads through the Andes Mountains.

Llamas are suitable as pack animals because of their firm feet and their ability to carry a third of their weight. You need to train your llama for packing before you use it for that purpose. *Alpacas* are not suitable for packing loads because of their relatively smaller weight.

Today, llamas are widely used by campers and adventurers to complement their outdoor activities. Hunters and fisherman have also seen the usefulness of llamas in their daily activities. They usually scout for their food and water while walking, although in harsh environments, you might need to pack food for them.

3. A source of fiber

Llamas and alpacas are an excellent source of fiber for yarns and fabric. Though farmers breed alpacas specifically for fiber because of their soft hair, llama hair also has its uses. Fleecing can be done only once a year, though.

Llama hair comprises a fine wool fiber intertwined with coarse guard hairs, but separating the coarse fibers from the fine wool can be quite the task! Once it is achieved, working with the wool becomes easier. This is why llama wools are expensive, generally selling for $2 per ounce.

The coarse hair of llamas is usually used to make rugs and ropes. Alpaca hair is soft, strong and lightweight, containing no lanolin, which makes it easy to be processed and cleaned without using chemicals. They produce more fiber than llamas despite the double hair-coat of llamas.

The fibers produced from these animals are regarded as luxury fibers and can be a superb source of income, given its growing popularity within the fiber industry. Besides the fantastic benefits you stand to gain, it is also a good financial investment.

4. Easy care

Feeding llamas is relatively easy compared to other grazing animals. You might think because they are large animals they require large quantities of food, but this is not the case. They are generally happy grazing pastureland and need not be fed much in the way of additional food. However, in the colder months, you will need to supplement their diet with grass and hay.

Given the right care and attention, llamas are generally a healthy breed. However, like most other large farm animals, they require routine checks to keep them in shape.

Proper grooming includes cleaning their feet to prevent lameness, and they should receive appropriate vaccines to prevent them from falling ill. Helped by your veterinary doctor, keeping your llamas and alpacas in good health should not be difficult.

5. Suitable for show animals

Llamas make great show animals because of their intelligence and ability to learn quickly. The Alpaca and Llama Show Association has hosted over 150 llama shows, an eventful time when hundreds of owners gather for competition.

The competition awards people for the training and breeding of the animals.

They can be easily trained to run obstacles, like dogs or horses. The show involves llamas navigating courses and running over obstructions like downed trees and rivers. They excel as show animals because of their herd mentality.

They are not shy or scared amidst large groups, especially in competition.

6. Small area is not a barrier

Like other animals, llamas and alpacas require adequate fencing, which will serve as protection for them. You don't have to possess a big parcel of land before you can set up where they will live, though; you can use a small space in your backyard to keep one or two.

Any form of shelter (natural or artificial) will suffice. A well-ventilated shelter will help keep them shaded and cool during hot seasons. An adequate shelter will also help keep them warm during the cold season, and the shelter will not cost you much compared to the value it provides your llamas.

7. They make great pets

Llamas are well-behaved animals, and they make great pets. They are generally used as pets because of their friendly disposition and cleanliness, making them an ideal companion for your children, provided they are cared for properly.

Some are skeptical about keeping them as pets because they spit, but typically, a llama will only spit when it has a dispute about food or when it feels threatened. Did you know, though – you can train a llama not to spit!

Another reason to keep them as pets is their healthy lifestyle, which requires only mild maintenance.

8. They are an excellent investment

Starting a llama and alpaca farm is a wonderful investment. With this addition to your farm, you will enjoy a tax deduction from the federal government; a unique tax benefit to people who train these animals.

A full-grown llama can sell for around $10,000! You will, however, need to be patient because they usually give birth only once a year. But, considering the minimal care and feeding you need to invest in them, you could stand to gain significantly from selling them.

You can make money from the fiber produced by the animals every year. Their hair is an excellent source of wool, and they grow in different colors. One ounce of llama wool sells for around $2.

Conclusion

Llamas are great animals to raise because of their wonderful personalities. From their companionship, beauty and intelligence, you will enjoy every bit of your experience with them. Knowing and understanding their outstanding characteristics, you should have no doubts about raising one – or even more!

Chapter 2: Llama Breeds and Alpacas

Quick Fact - *The easiest way to distinguish between an alpaca and a llama is size - llamas are typically twice as big as alpacas. Another way to know is by their ears - an alpaca's ears are short and pointy while a llama's ears are longer and stand up straight.*

Llamas and alpacas are often two creatures confused with each other. Differentiating these two creatures is more like telling a turtle from a tortoise.

These two exciting animals belong to a group called Camelids; a broad name given to animals that look like camels.

Animals in this family commonly have long necks. Although they feed on plants, they are not ruminants.

By simply looking at these animals, you can tell they are different. Anyone can spot their long thin legs and necks differ from those of goats, sheep or cows.

Their stomachs are divided into three parts, whereas a ruminant's stomach must have *four* parts.

However, just like ruminants, they also possess two toes. Their toes are unique, though, as they do not have hooves like ruminants.

Instead of hooves, their feet's soft pads give them a better grip on the ground.

The animals in this family are a little different from other animals as they are the only mammals known to have oval-shaped red blood cells. All other mammals have red blood cells shaped like disks.

Before you consider the variations between these two beautiful creatures, we need to be clear about something. There are two concepts commonly misused and understanding the two will help you better appreciate the variations between these two animals: the terms are *breeds* and *species.*

Species is a broad term that refers to a group of animals that look alike and can mate to produce offspring.

Let's use dogs as an example. You know that all dogs can mate and produce puppies; you also know that there are different types of dogs. Even with the different types, when you see a dog, you can tell it's a dog, not some other animal. With that picture in mind, the general name 'dog' refers to the species.

But *breeds* are the different types of animals *under the species.* Their appearance is usually different. Using the dog analogy from before, a *breed* would be a Pomeranian.

The Pomeranian and the Husky are different in appearance. Looking at them, you know they are dogs; they both bark and do what most dogs do. Both are of the same species (dogs). However, they are different breeds (Pomeranian and Husky).

Now that you get the picture, let's investigate the differences between llamas and alpacas.

Differences between Llamas and Alpacas

Nature almost always has two related animals that are hard to tell apart. Animals like toads and frogs, alligators and crocodiles, the list goes on. One of such wonders of nature is the llama and the alpaca.

The two animals look so much alike, it's challenging to tell them apart, unless you are an expert (or have read this book carefully!)

If you see these two animals together, these points will help you tell which is which.

1. Face

Starting with the most apparent part of the body, llamas usually have long faces compared with the alpacas. Alpacas usually have short faces with more fur than llamas. Some people think alpacas are cuter than llamas.

2. The Ears

The ears of the animals are probably the next noticeable difference. The ears of llamas are usually long, curved and shaped like bananas, whereas in alpacas, the ears are short, straight and typically pointy.

3. Size

This feature is a clear-cut distinction between the two animals. Alpacas are smaller than llamas and the average weight for an adult alpaca is between 45 and 70 kg (about 100-150 pounds).

Adult llamas usually grow to at least double that weight. The average weight of an adult llama is between 90 and 160 kg (about 200-350 pounds).

Also, llamas are usually taller than alpacas. The height is typically measured from the shoulder to the ground and, while alpacas rarely exceed 90 cm (35 inches) in height, llamas can grow as tall as 110 cm (45 inches) or even more.

4. Animal Fiber

You can also differentiate between the animals by touching them. Alpacas have fluffy, soft, and fine hair, while llamas have a rough coat.

Fiber gleaned from alpacas is used in making hats, shawls, and socks. People do not use wool from llama for making clothes unless it is from baby llamas.

5. Temperament

The temperament refers to the moods or general behavior of an animal. While alpacas are usually very gentle creatures, llamas are not.

You've probably heard these animals do spit, but this is usually only when they feel threatened. While it only happens on rare occasions, it's more common in llamas than with alpacas.

Alpacas move together as a herd, like sheep, while llamas are lone rangers, preferring their own company. For this reason and their size, llamas are used for guarding other animals.

Interestingly, they are used to guard alpacas because alpacas are nervous animals. Faced with danger, a guard llama will bravely use itself as a distraction.

6. Endurance

Due to their larger size, llamas have more endurance than alpacas, and also have firm feet which give them extra grip. Therefore, they are more suited to walking longer distances than alpacas and are typically used in desert and mountain regions.

Llamas can also carry as much as one-third of their body weight while alpacas are not suited to carrying packs or people.

You will find other differences in how the two animals are used. People usually raise llamas for their meat since their fur is not the best quality. They are also excellent when used as carriage animals or bred as guard animals.

Alpacas are reared mainly for their fur, which is of superior quality and grows faster than llama fur.

By now, you should be able to differentiate between alpacas and llama. Now, let's see the different breeds under the two species of animals.

Breeds of Llamas

There are four breeds of llamas. They are the classic llama, the Wooly llama, the Silky llama, and the Suri llama. The Classic llama is believed to be a major ancestor of the other three types. The other three are believed to have originated from extensive cross-breeding.

Of all four breeds, the Classic llama is the most common and also the largest. In contrast, Suri llama is the rarest and holds the reputation of being the smallest among the other breeds. The breeds look similar and sometimes differentiating them can be challenging.

All breeds have similar colors, which can be white, black, brown, red or beige; the colors can be plain, spotted or speckled. Therefore, identifying them is often by the characteristics of their fur and by their size.

Here is a brief description of the breeds.

Classic Llama

This is the most common breed, and the term *classic* refers to the saddle-like pattern of its coat. The hair on its back is longer than the hair on the rest of its body.

Their fleece is rough to the touch, although the undercoat, next to the skin, is fine. When you comb it, you can see the fine hairs are thin.

Llamas do not have as much fiber on their legs, neck and head, but some have hair on their necks, which looks similar to a mane.

The breed is bigger compared to other breeds.

Classic llamas are hardy animals, and they can do well in almost any type of weather. Even in freezing situations, unlike other breeds, classic llamas will thrive, but they will not do well in hot, humid conditions.

This breed of llamas shed their fur when you brush them, so they do not need shearing. However, in extremely hot temperatures, shearing helps keep them cool.

Silky Llama

These llamas are like the Wooly llama breed, but there are a few differences.

The breed is a cross between the Classic llama and the Wooly llama. They are also called *Medium llamas*. These animals typically have long hair around their body and neck and short hair on their heads, ears, and legs.

Their hair is shiny and has curls that frequently form locks. Their ever-growing hair has two layers; the top part is the guard hair, which is long and rough to touch while the undercoat is soft fleece.

Their shiny, curly hair gives the Silky llamas a beautiful appearance, but their curls and locks quickly get dirty. When they are out grazing in the field, the kinks in their hair can easily pick up lots of dirt – and it gets even worse when left un-sheared.

That can also happen when sheared incorrectly. For instance, barrel shearing, a popular method of sharing llamas, can also lead to dirty hair.

To prevent this, they should be sheared often. Frequent shearing will keep the curls and locks short and clean.

Wooly Llama

This breed of llama is usually smaller than other breeds, and their name comes from their appearance. They have thick wool covering their body, particularly around their head, ears and neck.

Depending on the individual animal, the amount of fiber can be small, medium, or thick. Its fiber is fluffy, lofty and thick, with curls and a few interlocks. While their fur is like the Silky and Suri llamas, the only difference is that theirs is softer and not as shiny.

The Wooly llamas have just a single layer of fur and do not have an undercoat. Typically, they have only a few guard hairs, which refers to the hair found on the outer coat of an animal. Guard hair is rough to the touch, and it keeps the llama dry by repelling water.

Because of their unique characteristics, their coats can be used as a replacement for alpaca fiber. The hair on Wooly llamas is always growing and, if you decide to raise this breed, you will need to shear them often. Your location will determine how often and the reason for shearing them.

In warmer environments, you must shear them at least once a year. That way, the animal will not suffer from the heat. If you raise them in cold conditions, consider sharing them once in two years. Shearing in colder environments will help prevent the fiber from forming clumps.

Suri Llama

"*Suri*" as a name was first used in describing alpacas. It became the name for this popular breed when people crossed llamas and alpacas. The word itself translates to the locks found in alpaca fibers.

These locks are a peculiar characteristic of this breed and are typically well defined, starting from the skin and ending at the tip of the hair strands. The locks in the Suri breed can be in different variations; the common ones look like corkscrews, while some are twisted.

When you hear the name, "Suri" the adjective "extreme" should come to mind. The hair on these animals is exceptionally smooth and shiny, short, soft and is similar to that of the Wooly llamas. The only difference is that the hair on the woolly llamas is a little finer than the Suri llama.

One problem with this breed, however, is there are few of them with about 100 in the whole of Europe and breeding is very difficult because there are so few.

Breeds of Alpacas

Now that you've learned about the different breeds of llamas, let's talk about alpacas. Unlike llamas, alpacas have only two known breeds.

These are the *Huacaya* breed and the *Suri* breed; the Haucayas being the most popular of the two breeds. As of today, there are about 3.7 million alpacas in the world. Almost 90% of this population is thought to be of the Huacaya breed.

Differentiating the breeds can be tricky, even more so than with llamas. Unlike with llamas, both breeds of alpacas are almost the same size, and both have the same preferences in terms of living conditions.

Continue reading to discover the unique characteristics of these two breeds.

Suri Alpaca

Like you already read, the name "Suri" is mainly used for the alpacas. According to archeologists, the breed is ancient, and research shows it could have existed for over 5000 years. Of the 3.7 million alpacas in the world, only about 370,000 are Suri alpacas.

The distinguishing feature of this breed is its fur. It is typically long with locks at the end, is shiny and dangles freely. Their hair is typically packed densely, is usually soft, and it feels greasy to the touch.

The hair covers the animals from their head to their toes. Interestingly, the hair is locked in all parts of their body, and besides the shiny appearance, the hair on the Suri Alpaca makes them look flat on the sides.

The fiber gleaned from the Suri breed is in high demand, with the highest demand coming from luxurious fashion stores. They use the fibers to produce luxury coats, sweaters, unique designer clothes and the choicest materials for interior decoration. Buyers often look for the shine as the primary characteristic of this quality product.

Huacaya Alpaca

You might have seen an alpaca that looks like a teddy bear, and it's likely you saw a Huacaya Alpaca breed. Their teddy bear appearance comes from their densely packed wavy hair.

In terms of size, they are not bigger than the Suri breed, but their fluffy hair makes them look bigger.

Their colors are similar to those in the Suri breed, but differ slightly. The hair of the Huacaya breed can come in different shades of gray, while Suri breeds do not produce those colors.

Besides the hair color, Huacaya alpacas do not have markings. Their hair is plain and of almost uniform colors, unlike their Suri counterparts. Suri alpacas always have unique spots on their hair called *Appaloosa* markings, in different colors, sizes and shapes. For instance, you might find a white Suri Alpaca with some dark marks. Those are called Appaloosa marks, and they are generally absent in Huacaya breeds.

The colorful fur of the Huacaya breed is also of high demand, like in the Suri breed. The hair is usually used for clothing worn close to the body, and its fleece is softer than the fleece from sheep.

Though Huacaya alpacas are mainly bred for their fibers, their skin is also in high demand, and is used in producing many high-quality leather products.

The meat from Huacaya alpacas has also become popular recently. The meat is tender, has a mild flavor, and nutritionally, it is one of the healthiest meats in the world. It is high in protein, and low in cholesterol, saturated fat, and calories.

The meat is served in expensive Peruvian restaurants across the world.

Other Closely Related Species

Just the way you have extended family members, alpacas and llamas have relatives. You might call them cousins.

Whichever name you choose, remember that these species are wild. They are considered wild because they do not stay around humans, preferring to live far away in the bush.

Due to their wild nature, little is known of these two species, known as the Guanaco and Vicuna species. The Guanaco's size lies between the llama and the alpaca and llamas are believed to have originated from them.

Similarly, alpacas are believed to have originated from the Vicunas. The Vicuna is light compared with the Guanaco, more delicate, and their fur commands a higher price. That explains why they are an endangered species in many countries.

With current advanced methods of breeding, some of these species have been crossed, resulting in offspring which have been given various names, often a combination of the parental breed names.

Now armed with all the historical and scientific knowledge about these breeds, let's move on to learning how to raise a llama or alpaca. In the following chapter, you will learn about the facilities and housing you need before obtaining one of these animals.

Chapter 3: Facilities, Land, and Housing Requirements for Raising Llamas and Alpacas

Quick Fact - *The average llama weighs 280 to 450 pounds. They can carry between 25% and 30% of their own body weight so a male llama, for example, weighing in at 400 pounds, can carry between 100 and 120 pounds on a 10 to 12-mile trek without breaking a sweat.*

It's easy to get carried away with the excitement of starting a llama or alpaca farm. However, be sure to consider the one thing that matters most - *where to keep them.*

Note that the original habitat for this member of the camel family is in the arid, high altitude region of South America. However, if you know how to go about it, you can run a successful llama or alpaca farm in *any* area. This book will show you how.

Fortunately, preparing a home for the llamas or alpacas is not as difficult a task as it may seem. If you already have a barn on your property, you can start from there. However, you need to consider the barn's structure and determine if it will work for the animals. If not, you will need to build a new facility to house them.

When planning a new structure to house your new pets, your priority must always be the animal's safety, health, and comfort. As their caretakers, convenience comes into play. Considering these themes when planning and building the structure will result in a thriving farming experience.

Indoor Housing Requirements for Llamas

Llamas and alpacas, by nature, can cope with most types of weather. However, for health and comfort, they require shelter from the wind, sun and rain. Loving – and needing – shade, large trees on your property will help protect your animals. However, if you have little tree coverage, a three-sided self-built shed will do, serving as a shield from the wind and the sun and providing a good place to train and handle your llamas or alpacas.

When considering the type of shelter needed, remember that freedom is a treasure for llamas and alpacas; they thrive on the freedom to come and go. Therefore, provide a shelter that gives the feeling of openness, using large windows and doors instead of dark sheds, which makes them feel shut in.

During the summer, llamas or alpacas may suffer heatstroke when the temperature and humidity rise so high. For this season, have sprinklers or misters to maintain their body temperature and help them cope with the climatic condition.

When it's the rainy season, and the ground becomes wet and soggy for an extended period, llamas need a place in their shelter where they can dry their feet every day. Also, this place serves as hay storage and water for continuous feeding. Foot-rot, though not common to llamas and alpacas, is caused by standing water, and is slow to heal.

Finally, in any climatic condition, it is best to have at least one stall where you can confine newborn babies and their mothers. The same goes for an ailing member of the herd for treatments. During the cold or damp season, wall-mounted lamps can help keep newborns warm.

Keep a close eye on baby llamas for at least the first two weeks after birth, especially when born during extreme weather conditions. During this period, they learn about their environment and seek comfort.

Outdoor Living Requirements for Llamas

Llamas or alpacas need enough room to stretch and run. However, the required amount of outdoor space for keeping llamas isn't definite. While some farmers believe you can successfully maintain a llama herd with little or no space and a well-designed barn, some say at least half an acre is needed to give them the freedom they require.

But then, the balance to both schools of thought rests on the number of llamas and the type of farming you practice.

You can keep them indoors throughout the grooming days, and they'll turn out fine. You can also provide them with outdoor space to stretch and run. However, regardless of the type of farming you maintain, you need one or more large gates to allow the free movement of humans and equipment onto the farm premises.

Moving sick llamas or alpacas can be challenging. Therefore, a large gate that will enable the movement of vehicles – like tractors and a transport trailer - in and out is a must.

To offer enough outdoor space for them as a playground, consider a well-drained field. Llamas and alpacas dislike wet areas and will neither stand nor lay on a muddy, wet surface. If possible, raise the outer apron and interior floor with sand, decomposed granite, or crushed rock.

Indoor and Outdoor Space Requirement

Barn space need not be large. However, you can plan by building a large barn when starting. That's because it's cost effective to have a large barn and allows your herd grow in number easily.

If you build a small barn from the onset, when your herd expands, there will be a non-negotiable need for more room, costing more than you had budgeted for. Best to consider building a larger-than-needed barn from the beginning.

Regardless of the size of the barn you build, it must have enough space to feed them. Also, include a space for catch pens in the barn's layout. Those spaces are reserved for important chores like animal grooming and administering of vaccines. They can also be useful when you need to separate and monitor sick llamas or alpacas and a place for your veterinarian to use during calls.

If you have or can spare some extra space, you can create a compartment to store hay and supplies. This method protects the hay from the weather and other animals and allows it to stay dry.

However, be careful about storing the hay close to the animal's barn; during a fire, excess hay becomes a propellant and accelerant and can promote fire. Smoking and other fire-related activities should be done a safe distance from your hay stores.

The time you spend in planning your llama's shelter is time well-spent; a critical step to the maintenance and growth of happy and healthy llama or alpaca herds.

Barn and Shed Layout

As previously stated, llamas or alpacas are best kept in a three-sided barn or shelter. Here are a few tips that will help you in constructing this:

• Your shed should face east

The open side of the shed should face the east, as this direction is the most moderate in terms of weather.

• Create more than one door to the outside

Where you have more than a few llamas or alpacas, especially when you have more females, ensure you have more than one door to the outside because the "herd queen" likes to lie by the door. If there's only one door, it can prevent other llamas from accessing the outside. Avoid closing barn doors completely, as they need an escape route in the case of fire.

• Consider proper cross-ventilation

Add enough windows and openings for proper cross ventilation. Besides, a barn with plenty of doors and openings will remain cleaner.

• Cover the barn doors with hanging plastic

In winter months, you can cover the barn doors with hanging plastic, like you see at loading docks. It will protect them from rain, snow, and wind while still allowing them to go in and out without obstruction.

• Install air vents at the peak of the roof

Hot air rises toward the ceiling, so plan a high ceiling design so warm air can rise above the animals. Also, install air vents at the peak of the roof for the free outflow of hot air.

• Install fans for the summer season

Fans installed on the ceiling of barns help move hot air out of the barn and increase air circulation. Therefore, attach the fans to the barn ceiling at strategic points to blow directly at the animals.

• Install automatic heaters and water dispensers

You can include an automatic water dispenser in the barn plan and install a water heater to prevent freezing during the winter seasons. It could be a future installation but provide room for it when designing the barn.

• Use concrete flooring

You can use sand, Ag-lime, or concrete for the barn floor. However, for ease of cleaning, it's best to use a concrete floor as this can be easily cleaned by hosing down regularly.

For cushioning, cover the bathing area with a rubber mat. It also prevents wool from rubbing thin on the animal's knees.

The concrete flooring should have a rough finish to help keep the animal's toenails trimmed. Besides, a smooth surface can become slippery when dirty or wet.

• Consider Ag-Lime as a good flooring alternative

Ag-Lime, also called B-Lime, is another flooring type that works well in the shelter. Though it's a smooth powdery substance, it packs down like a hunk of concrete.

You can also use it in areas where llamas will pace, such as right outside the barn or gate opening. You'll find it useful as it prevents mud, making it easy to clean.

• Build a shallow wooded feeding trough

Along the walls of the barn, build a wood feeding trough – and make it shallow. This allows you to spread out the feed so they don't get too large a mouthful which can be a choking hazard.

Please make sure all animals get equal access to feed. Also, plan for a grain storage area for easy access to animal food.

Use metal storage containers that can prevent raccoons from getting in and gobbling up your grains.

• Use barn dividers

Use a twelve or sixteen-foot tall gate as the barn divider. Mount it on the wall so you can easily remove it if you need to make the area bigger or design it so you can swing it to one side to get a bobcat or cart into the space for cleaning.

• Build a hay feeder

Locate a hay feeder outside of the barn. It will encourage the animals to leave their shelter. However, ensure you cover the hay feeder to prevent the hay from getting wet from rain or overnight dew.

During the wet season, you can feed them hay inside the barn; remember, though, that requires more cleaning.

• Plan an area for storage

Plan an area where you can store halters or head-collars, groom supplies, and medical equipment.

You can also store hay over the llama's pens, but you must plan for an opening that allows you to drop the hay bales directly over the area you need. Again, try to store hay away from the animal barn because it can support fire outbreaks. It's best to keep hay in another barn or shelter and avoid smoking in the barns.

Finally, note that not all the points and items suggested above may be right for you, but these ideas can support how you plan your barn and make your herd management successful.

Fencing and the Environment

The reason you need fencing around your farm is more about guarding against predators than keeping llamas or alpacas contained. Predators include coyotes, cougars, and dogs.

Dogs cause most of the predator attacks to llamas. Therefore, when planning or fencing your farm, your focus should be to guard against dogs; a fence that keeps out dogs will also keep out coyotes.

Dealing with the cougars is another ball game. A cougar will climb through any fencing if determined to do so; luckily, though, cougar attacks are rare. You should, therefore, focus more on controlling dog attacks, which are more common.

There are several fencing styles, and various types of materials can be used in building fences. However, when deciding the type of enclosure and materials to make your fence, functionality should be your determining factor.

Wire fencing is inexpensive. If you prevent it from getting buried in the soil, it can last for a long time. Border rail fences are also a good fencing option, but you will need to back them up with wire fencing. Combined, these two will effectively guard your farm against predators.

Avoid the use of barbed wire; while it might be adequate to keep predators out, it's dangerous to your herd. Any inattentive or curious llama can run into the fence or rub against it and get injured by the barbs.

A "No-Climb" fence is popular because it is safe, costs less, and has small openings. It's difficult for predators to climb because it's high.

You can install a "No-Climb" fence on metal, wood, or fiberglass post. It's the type of fence that keeps out almost all types of unwanted animals. Even animals that do not directly prey on llamas or alpacas can carry parasites or infectious diseases and should be kept away from your farm.

Another common type of fencing among alpaca and llama farmers is the "Multi-strand high tensile fencing." It is a type of fence that has multiple strands of variably-spaced wires. The wire is concentrated at the bottom and sparsely distributed at the top; this design stops predators from digging for access to the farm and prevents your llamas or alpacas from getting their heads stuck in the wire.

When constructing the fence, use treated wooden posts, metal, or a combination of both, spacing them about 8 to 12 feet apart. A five-foot-high fence is good enough, but remember that a motivated adult llama can jump a high fence. Even if that happens, the llamas or alpacas won't move far from the company of others, and you can easily entice them back with treats.

Cement the posts supporting braces, pulling posts, and corners to the ground. If your farm is on land that's not solid, you may need to cement *all posts*. Remember that it is more economical to build a strong and safe fence from the onset than to mend or rebuild flimsy ones when they can no longer keep predators out of the farm.

Climatic Demands on Housing and Facilities

There are slight changes in housing and facilities demands as seasons come and go. Therefore, you need to familiarize yourself with the changes and know what to do during each season.

• Winter Requirements

A common misconception is that a llama's native habitat is a high-altitude, cold region. Although the native habitat has proximity to the equator, it provides an average temperature of 20 to 55 degrees F. While the temperature does drop at night, it rarely goes below 10 degrees F. With this in mind, farmers who nurture llamas or alpacas in a cold region will need to protect them.

A large, enclosed barn is the best protection when the temperature falls below 0 degrees. Enclose the barn with hanging plastic to reduce wind.

Llamas or alpacas with less wool will need special consideration during the cold; they must be watched for signs of hypothermia. Consider insulating and heating the barns as commonly done for livestock during winter. However, if you are going to enclose the barn, ensure adequate ventilation. You can install air vents at the peak of the roof for the free in/outflow of air.

Humidity can quickly build up in the barn, causing an outbreak of bronchitis and pneumonia within the herd.

As an alternative to heating the barn, you can encourage body heat by forcing the herd to cluster together in the shed or barn.

• Summer Requirements

In warm climates, shade – either in the form of built shed or trees – is essential, as llamas or alpacas dislike heat; high temps and humidity can cause heatstroke.

Large or normal circulating fans have also proven to be useful when indoor living spaces such as the barn get too hot.

In the heat, llamas and alpacas will stretch out in the sun, but they often find a means of cooling themselves, such as under a shade tree.

You can help them manage the heat throughout the hot summer seasons by providing them with a means of cooling, such as ponds, streams, wading pools, sprinklers, misters, etc. You can also provide a shaded area with sand where they can lay.

It would be best if you had accommodations in place before you consider raising a llama. With the suggestions and requirements outlined above, you should not find it hard to put such facilities in place, and maintain it based on the seasons.

Once you have all your housing facilities, you are ready to buy your first llama. The next chapter will teach you how to make the best choice for you.

Chapter 4: Buying Your First Llama

Quick Fact – *Llamas are incredibly social animals and don't like to be alone. The social structure can change quickly in a herd; a male llama can change position in the herd by winning or losing fights with the herd leader.*

Now you're ready to buy your first llama so you have many factors to consider and steps to take. Llamas and alpacas are spectacular animals, and understanding these animals is important before setting off to buy your own.

Buying a llama becomes more straightforward once you clearly understand these unique animals.

Things to Do and Consider When Buying Your First Llama

Llama-keeping can be likened to finding a new hobby; there are different aspects you must get acquainted with and rules to keep. Buying a llama isn't a decision to make because you're feeling blue or lonely, or on a whim. It must be a slow, thoughtful, and knowledgeable process. Here's a list of suggestions to help you in this important decision.

1. Research

Researching the animal and its care is crucial before investing in one. It's essential that you digest all the available information and possibly visit a llama farm to acquaint yourself with what owning one might be like.

It will also help you discover if the space where you intend to house them in is wide enough, or if you'll be paying a farm to house and care for it. After your research, you can determine if llama-keeping is a venture you are capable of undertaking.

2. Determine Why You Are Buying Llamas

Don't buy a llama just because you feel like it, or because you like how they look. You might be setting yourself up for more than you bargained. If you're looking to breed llamas, then you should look for females rather than geldings.

You'll need to determine how old your llama should be and what it weighs, if you will keep them as pets, for parking, or cart driving. In all, you should have a specific reason in mind for buying one, as it will help you decide what you need.

3. Where You'll Be Buying From

The excitement of owning a llama, after months – or maybe years – of waiting, should not make you jump on the first opportunity to buy one. Where you're buying your llama is as important as how you'll care for it. You need the history of the llama's life and behavior.

A random llama seller might not provide you with all the information you need to care for it. That's why it's best to buy from a trusted breeder rather than brokers or an auction. You risk not getting the type needed for the purpose you intend, and worse, it could be sickly.

4. Space

Like any other herd animal, llamas need sufficient space and room to roam. If your backyard space isn't very large, you may still house two llamas there. However, if you love llamas but you don't have enough room to accommodate them, then you can consider boarding them with the local breeders near you.

Some ranches may house them, so all you need to do your homework before purchasing your llama. If you can't find one available, your seller might board your animals, so you can still a proud llama owner – even if you're short on space.

5. Consider the Herd-Nature of Llamas

It's okay to fall in love with these intelligent animals and want to bring them home. However, note that they are only at their best when other llamas are around.

So, if you are thinking of buying a llama, you will probably need to go home with at least two same-sex llamas. You can also board them with others until you buy your next llama.

You may buy just one, only if it'll be serving as a guard to your sheep herd.

6. Time and Care

One secret behind the calmness of llamas is attention and care. It will help if you have plenty of time to care for its needs. These animals need at least one monthly routine vet check, regular fur-shearing, and nail-trimming.

When you're getting a llama, you need to pour all the love you can into its care. Your llama will feel more confident around you when it receives care and attention from you.

Ensure that you have the time to check up on them to ascertain they are in good condition. If you're too busy and can't get someone to do these things in your absence, then you might want to reconsider keeping one.

Dos and Don'ts When Buying Your First Llama

There are so many things to consider when you want to buy llamas. The rules may seem overwhelming at first, but it's all for your sanity and the wellbeing of the animals you're buying.

There are certain dos-and-don't that will help make your purchase go smoothly. Here is a list for your consideration:

- Never buy a llama without educating yourself

Knowing all you need to know about llamas puts you at an advantage when you eventually buy one. You need to have the right knowledge as you risk trouble if you purchase without adequately understanding these unique animals.

- Never buy your first llama without observing it

Observing it doesn't mean lifting it, turning its back down and legs up, to do a thorough check. It means spending time visiting a llama farm to watch how llamas live, how they are taken care of, and how they behave.

Observing means you know everything that goes on around the farm every time you visit. See how the animals are led, trained, haltered, and managed. It will show you what you're venturing into and help you imagine yourself doing the same thing.

- Don't forget to ask questions

You need all the information you can get; therefore, it's essential to visit the farm as many times as possible. You'll be able to ask questions about anything that you don't understand, and possibly spot the llama or llamas you wish to buy.

You'll need to ask questions about the health records of the animals as they give a possible indication of the health status of your prospective purchase. Ask about how they are vaccinated, how often, about the vet, and what to expect after buying one. Some farms will offer free breeding, follow-up, or even delivery. Do not pay for a llama until everything is fully spelled out.

- Do a pre-purchase examination

Have a vet help examine the animals before you purchase; it's always easier to take a professional's word than that of the person looking to sell the llama. A pre-purchase examination by a vet makes the whole process easier and even helps to spot problems that the seller might be unaware of.

- Don't purchase your first llama from an auction

It's usually unwise to purchase your first llama from an auction. It's a risky venture for many reasons. Purchasing your first llama from an auction won't afford you the privilege to observe, check, and ask questions like you'd have done if you were buying from a farm. A lot might go wrong with the animal after purchasing it, and you might not have access to its health records. Plus, you might never get to know if the animals were auctioned due to an underlying problem. Finally, it will be difficult to ascertain if the animal is the best fit for what you had in mind.

- Pay attention to the personality of the llama you're buying

Like humans, llamas also have their unique personalities, strengths, and weaknesses. Seek to discover those and possibly ask the seller once you spot a pair of llamas want to take home. Don't fall for the trick of believing that there is a perfect llama. Your job is to get acquainted with the possible difficulties buying a particular type might bring and ask yourself if *you're willing to deal with them.*

- Never buy just one llama

Llamas hate to be alone, turning mean and depressed when out of the herd. You don't want an unhappy llama around you. So, never buy a single llama!

Any seller willing to sell only one to you, despite knowing that you've never owned one, should be avoided. They are probably interested in your money and not in your sanity, much less the llama's wellbeing.

- Don't buy a pair (male and female)

The possibility of buying a male and female might seem like a juicy idea, especially if you're looking to raise a herd to sell later. However, consider that a male and female kept together will repeatedly breed, a practice that will eventually lead to infections for both animals. If you're looking to breed, it's better to buy same-sex pairs.

There's no point purchasing opposite-sex pairs if you aren't interested in breeding in the first place.

- Don't buy a llama you've never seen

It's normal to get deals off the internet and even be furnished with enough information to help you make a decision. However, it's better to seek a seller if they are around your locality. Please don't buy a llama off the internet that you've never seen, touched, or observed.

- Visit several llama farms

You deserve the best deal for your money and won't possibly get that visiting only a single breeder. Visit many llama farms, observe their practices, and familiarize yourself with their terms before buying.

- Don't purchase a llama without a written contract

A written contract keeps the seller accountable for all the post-sales services promised. Having the agreement in writing makes it easier to refer to the terms when things go wrong, rather than guessing what was agreed upon.

You can more easily hold the seller responsible to fulfill his part of the contract when it's written in a contract.

How to Spot a Good Llama Breed to Buy

Now that you know all you need to do and not do when buying your first llama, you're ready to go! These crucial points will help you know the right llama breed to buy.

1. The Reputation of the Breeder

The breeder's reputation will help determine what breed of llama to buy. Therefore, it is essential to check with many breeders and observe their practices. A breeder of repute will be a member of llama associations and have their animals registered on the international llama registry.

The breeder will also breed young llamas responsibly without mass-producing them like dog pups. Anywhere you find more than a maximum of five *crias* (baby llamas or alpacas) in a breeding farm, it indicates that the breeder may not be caring for their animals properly.

2. The Seller has Good Knowledge and Record of the Animals

How a seller engages with his llamas will reflect the quality of care they've received and helps you to decide if the investment is worth it. How much knowledge the seller displays about the animal's health and history will also help to determine the choice you make.

A good breed will reflect a long history of attention and care from the seller, and the risk of future problems after purchase will be minimal.

3. Quality of Veterinary Attention

The quality of veterinary attention that the llama breed has received over time will help you determine what quality you're paying for. If the llamas are regularly vaccinated, routinely checked, and have an overall record of good health, then you know you've found a good breed.

4. Excellent Conditions from Observation

What you observed during your visits will also determine if you've found the right breed. Consider whether the animals look healthy or underweight, have clean bodies, have sores or other apparent indicators of how well they were cared for.

Were you able to take them for a walk? How did the animals respond to being led or haltered? Have they been trained? These steps provide necessary indicators for determining if you've found the right breed or if you should continue looking, depending on how you intend to use them. If they look sickly, malnourished, unkempt with untrimmed nails, and un-sheared fur, those might be the red flags for considering looking for a new place to buy from.

5. The Llamas are Independent

Now, the llamas may develop a liking for you when you show up around them consistently; still, they shouldn't be following you about!

When the animals are too friendly around you, then you shouldn't go for those breeds. It's dangerous for them to always want to be around you; they are livestock, not dogs.

When the llamas are friendly yet independent, consider them. The seemingly too-nice ones can turn out quite mean – especially when they don't get the attention they expect.

6. Sufficient Weaning and Milking

First, go for breeds weaned appropriately in five to six months. Breeds weaned earlier may be underweight, prove dangerous, and prone to infection and diseases later.

If you're looking for a female and intend to breed her, it's essential to find one whose mother milked well. If the mother was a light milker, she might also be a light milker which can pose problems for you later.

7. Good Genetic History

An expensive llama with an excellent genetic history will yield more overall benefits than a cheaper one with a history of genetic problems. Therefore, it's essential to ask your breeder about possible genetic problems in your prospective llamas.

How to Get a Good Deal on Your First Llama

Finally, it's time to get your first llama, but you're not sure about pricing; you can get a good deal on your first llama without emptying your purse.

Llama prices will always fall within three categories - cheap, moderately priced, and expensive. These animals vary in price due to quality of care, age, and individual breeder ratings. Some breeders offer an all-inclusive post-sale service, which might also create higher prices.

A free or cheap llama often has several reasons for being inexpensive, and you should find out why they are being sold for less.

On average, llamas should cost between $1500 and $5000. Finding a llama way lower than that amount shouldn't excite you so much as make you *curious*. Once you've been filled in on the condition of the llama and you are content with dealing with all the possible outcomes from that purchase, then you can move ahead.

Many factors determine your moderately-priced purchase. These factors include the age, quality of breeding, healthiness, weight, and strength of the llama. Checking prices with several farms will help you note if a seller is unreasonably hiking prices. But generally, well-bred llamas won't cost a fortune.

Some llamas will cost more, especially if you'll be boarding them with the seller because of lack of space or herd. You'll need to pay for all the care, feeding, and medical care. A pregnant llama will cost more than a non-pregnant female.

Carefully consider all the factors underlying your purchase as it determines how much you pay. Llama prices are relative from place to place, but ensure you're looking out for quality animals when seeking the best deals.

Conclusion

Buying a llama is not child's play, and you must be ready to undertake all the sacrifices in exchange for the thrill of owning these intelligent animals. Remember, if you are coming home with your first llama, it shouldn't be with just one llama, *but two*.

Ensure you have all it takes to host two or more llamas and prepare yourself mentally and financially for your new furry friends. Now that you know how to purchase and house a llama, you must learn their behaviors.

Chapter 5: Llama Behavior and Handling

Quick Fact – Llama's rarely bite. However, they will spit when upset or agitated, but usually at one another, not at people. They also neck wrestle and kick each other when upset, but they don't tend to attack humans – unless you upset them.

You need to know everything about llama behavior to properly care for them. It's important to be able to predict and understand their reactions. Interestingly, llamas are easy animals to care for, especially when you know how they behave.

In this chapter, you will discover everything you need to know about their behavior and ways to handle them. Now, let's dive in!

What Behaviors Does a Llama Exhibit?

A llama is an intelligent animal that can be easily trained; with one to five repetitions, they will learn and remember many skills. You can instruct them to do lots of things, such as accepting a halter and being led on a lead.

They can quickly adapt to training like pulling a cart, carrying a pack, and getting into and out of a carriage vehicle. Llamas are friendly animals, but they need the companionship of their kind.

Llamas are gentle, shy and curious animals; they are calm and have common sense, making them easy for anyone, even children, to handle. Llamas are enjoyable animals, and they are fun when doing things; however, most are not attention seekers and do not like to be handled excessively.

Do Llamas Spit?

Yes, llamas can spit, and it is one way they communicate with each other and display anger. Other means of communication with each other include ear position, humming, and body language.

Llamas usually spit at other llamas to establish dominance, but do not spit at people. If llamas spit at other llamas while in the barn, it is usually at feeding time when personal space gets invaded.

Llamas also spit as a defense mechanism. However, before they spit, they usually elongate their necks and heads upwards to show displeasure – that's their warning sign. If you read this body language correctly, you can steer clear!

Llamas won't spit at you unless they feel confined or perceive that they are in danger. Like dogs don't bite people without reason, these animals only spit when provoked as a defensive mechanism.

Llamas make a "mwa" or groaning sound to show anger or fear and put their ears back when agitated. You can also know how agitated the llama is from the content in the spit. When they are very disturbed, they draw materials from their innermost stomach, bringing up green, sticky cud from its depths. Try not to get caught in the path when llamas spit because it can get incredibly nasty!

When you train these animals correctly, llamas will rarely spit at a human. They might sometimes spit at each other to discipline lower-ranked llamas, as they are social herd animals. Llamas can climb the social ladder in their ranks by picking fights. You'll mostly witness these fights between male llamas to get the alpha position.

These fights between llamas can be entertaining. They spit, ram each other with their chests, wrestle with their necks, and kick to knock the other off balance. The female llamas usually spit to control other herd members.

You remember we talked about the llamas' need for the companionship of its kind. Now let's talk about companionship.

Companionship

As a herd animal, a llama needs other llamas. Therefore, you should have, at the very least, at least two llamas in your pasture. It is sad to see a llama alone, and even if you want the llamas to guard your sheep, get at least two for that purpose, as they are more effective when working with a companion. Their keen eyesight helps them remain vigilant of their surroundings and they have a natural curiosity, which makes them want to see and sniff everything.

Berserk Males

One cannot discuss llama behavior without touching on Berserk Male Syndrome, also known as "Novice Handler Syndrome" or "Berserk Alpaca Syndrome." It is a behavioral syndrome caused by humans when they incorrectly interact with young males (llama). The llama can exhibit aggressive behavior and humans misinterpret the aggressive behavior as friendliness.

Fast Runners

Llamas can run fast. The average dog can move at about 30 to 40 kilometers per hour; a llama, when it gets a sprint on, can move at over 60 kilometers an hour. This a great protective mechanism as it means they can outrun many predators.

Mating

When discussing llama behavior, mating is a topic you will hear a lot about. You should not hinder an aggressive male during mating as he will be preoccupied with completing his task and you could easily get hurt.

When you add the elements of different environments and females, you will see more differences in the llama male temperament. However, it is not only llama males with temperament variations. Female llamas also exhibit moodiness, and an untrained female llama's personality might change when a male approaches for mating. Even the crabbiest llama can turn sweet and docile during the mating session.

There are always llamas watching as spectators during mating. Any untrained female will lay close to the mating couple while the trained females will usually stay back and watch as if the process is for their entertainment.

Pregnancy

Pregnant llamas also change their personality. A friendly llama can become aloof, while a quiet and quirky llama can become spunky. They are affected by the change in hormones, and you can see it in the dramatic shift in their behaviors.

How Do They Communicate? Llama Sounds

Being herd animals, llamas communicate using several sounds.

1. Llama Humming

These animals use this sound to communicate from birth, similar to human humming. Llamas make this sound when worried, distraught, tired, anxious, or curious. A mother llama may also hum to welcome her newborn. This sound helps them communicate and stay connected.

2. Clucking

This sound is like a human clicking their tongue on the roof of their mouth. When llamas cluck, they typically hold back their ears. This sound expresses concern or signals friendliness, use it to greet new llamas or flirt with females.

3. Llama Ogling

This sound is like a person is gargling. Male llamas make this sound when going close to a female for breeding. It continues to sound that way until the copulation completes, and may go on for twenty minutes to an hour.

4. Llama Alarm Call

Llamas make this call when they sense fear or get surprised by something. The sound is loud, high-pitched, and rhythmic, and alerts others in the herd that a predator is nearby (especially dogs).

Llamas travel in herds when they are in the wild. When one animal notices a predator, they make this sound to alert the others.

5. Snorting

Llamas will snort when another llama is invading their space, usually as a warning message to move away. Not all llamas snort, but the ones that do snort often.

6. Screaming

When a llama screams, it is as if someone is blowing a siren next to your ear because they are loud! Llamas will scream only when they are not handled correctly. They also communicate their moods with a series of tail, body, and ear postures.

Just like humans, llamas are unique. Not all are smart, nice, or agreeable, and figuring out the core behavior of a llama will help you modify their behavior, or at least accommodate it.

Llama Handling

Although llamas are not animals to be overly-pampered, there are still guidelines you need to follow when handling them. To an extent, llamas are emotional animals and, as members of the camelid family, they have several traits similar to the camel. This means you can use camel treatment guidelines to handle your llamas.

Llamas are herding animals, making them averse to separation. One way to handle such a situation is to keep dividing the llamas into smaller groups. You will need to repeat this process until you select the one you need from a relatively small group. Be careful so as not to threaten or scare the animals, avoid sudden movements.

If you must remove just one llama from its herd for treatment or another purpose, specific procedures must be followed.

How Can I Separate One?

Try to approach the llama slowly and get hold of its head. Do not be forceful, but try to ensure a firm grip using your arm and shoulder. The llama may try to keep you from taking it – and sometimes in a forceful manner but there are a few tricks you can use in restraining it.

You can apply the earing technique: press down the head of the llama and firmly hold its outer ear. This technique is commonly used on camels and horses.

Also, you can press down the shoulder of the llama, placing your hands firmly at the neck base.

The midline catch is another brilliant way to catch them. The llama should be in a position where it aligns with the pen with its head in a corner. This positioning gives a smooth and steady movement from a place behind the eye. Place the back of your hand on its lower neck and then slide the hand up behind the ears as you step in to bring the other hand under the chin. Place your forefinger and thumb into the groove of the lower jaw, giving you a *bracelet hold* on it. The grip helps to keep the animal steady.

Some llamas can be cornered and grabbed around the neck for husbandry, but are likely to make a run for it. You can use a catch rope and wand to catch the animal without trapping it and entering its flight zone. When you do, the llama stands still. At that point, you can move closer. However, be aware of the llama's body position, then approach.

With the rope around its neck, you will be at a vantage point to help the animal gain balance and behavior properly. Maintain a safe distance from the llama. With this stance, you will not be a threat to it.

In handling llamas, you will need equipment that can be easily bought or improvised. Ropes are the most common equipment.

Do not use the rope for holding the animal still; instead, keep it tight enough to shut off its escape route. It might trigger the flight instinct in the animal, so it's best to use the pen as containment for the animal – not the rope.

Put your arm around the neck to maintain its balance; being pulled off balance by a handler creates panic in the animal. A llama in balance will carry about 67 percent of its bodyweight over the front. The remaining 33 percent will be over the rear legs with the head held in line over the neck and shoulders.

How Do I Treat Llamas?

The above procedures will allow you to complete your examination without unnecessary stress. Injections can be given in the triceps, or in the angle of the neck and shoulder but, when injecting the llama, lean over the animal so movement will not displace the needle.

When you carry out a blood test on your llama, crouch down to do it as this position will conceal quick and sudden movements that might frighten off the animal.

Llamas pose handling challenges because of their size and strength. Those with less-dense fleece are easier to examine, but if a llama cannot stand still for necessary procedures such as brushing, it likely will not be calm during veterinary processes.

In such cases, you can apply the techniques explained earlier, to give the animal the chance to stand independently.

How Do I Fix a Halter for Llamas?

A well-designed halter is recommended to help your animals balance effectively. It is a comfortable and useful tool used in communicating with camelid animals, especially the llama.

Camelids breathe through their nose. For this reason, you should use halters that do not slip forward on the nose, compressing the nasal cartilage. To prevent such incidents, tightly secure the crown piece behind the llama's ears. The halter you choose must be comfortable. You will know it is comfortable when there is enough room in the nose cavity for the llama to eat and ruminate. A perfect halter sits comfortably on the llama's head rather than on its nose.

Sometimes, it may seem impossible to conduct an examination, and thus, you require alternative plans. Do not chase your frightened animal; you may be risking an injury to yourself and/or the llama.

If necessary, reschedule examinations rather than putting your animal (or yourself) at risk. Get assistance from more experienced handlers or, in more serious cases, sedate it.

With these simple procedures in place, handling them will not be a problem. Taking time to study llamas will help you know how to deal with them in any situation.

Chapter 6: Llama Nutrition and Feeding

Quick Fact – *Llamas are vegetarian, and their digestive systems are incredibly efficient. They have three compartments in their stomachs – the rumen, the omasum, and the abomasum. They regurgitate their food and re-chew it several times to completely digest it, a process called chewing the cud.*

Llamas belong to a group of animals called the New World Camelid. Nutrition and feeding are unique because they have a significantly different digestive system from that of a typical ruminant, with a higher digestibility coefficient.

In this chapter, we will explore the llama digestive system, their nutritional requirements, and feeding recommendations, briefly exploring things you shouldn't feed them.

The Llama Digestive System

You might be wondering why it is essential to understand their digestive system. Llamas are not considered true ruminants. They are a modified ruminant because they have one stomach with three compartments compared to the true ruminants, which have four compartments.

Llamas only chew their food enough to mix it with saliva to lubricate the food and help it pass down the esophagus to the first compartment called the rumen. The esophagus is directly connected to the rumen and, in adult animals, may be as long as four feet.

The first compartment is about 83% of the total stomach volume; itis full of bacteria, and it is where the fermentation process begins. This bacteria is crucial to their nutrition, so if you upset the population of the bacteria, it can negatively affect their health.

You must be careful what you feed them and how you make changes to their diet. There is a water-like substance in this compartment which breaks down the cells of the plants and absorbs the nutrients; an imbalance might spell trouble for your llama's digestion.

The substance in the first compartment moves to the second compartment for further fermentation. Little activity happens here, and the second compartment is about 6% of the total stomach volume.

The third is full of stomach acid, which aid in the digestion of food. The stomach acid splashes on the cell membranes of the substance eaten, and once the cell bursts, it disperses the nutrients and energy from the food.

The bacteria that aided the fermentation process in the first and second compartments will be digested in the third compartment. It provides protein and is also a major source of amino acids.

The pH in the first and second compartments is neutral, while in the third compartment, it is acidic. Therefore, llamas can develop ulcers if they are not adequately fed. The nitrogen balance in their stomach is also crucial. They recycle urea so the bacteria in the stomach can synthesize the protein.

Llamas chew their food in a figure-eight motion. Once llamas chew and swallow their food, it goes to the other compartments of the stomach. The llamas then regurgitate their food and chew it again, repeating the process up to 75 times.

If you closely observe your llama, you will notice a bubble-like lump (known as the cud) moving up its neck. Therefore, regurgitating is known as *chewing the cud*.

It is essential to keep their digestive system in balance. Llamas needs microorganisms to break down cellulose, protein and urea and to keep them healthy; the microbe's population must not be upset.

What does this mean? If you are taking them to another farm or a new environment, provide them with the food they were used to eating and then slowly add new feed to its diet. If they will be doing strenuous activities, it is crucial not to change their diet. You can also add probiotics to ease their stress. A balanced and healthy microbial population in the stomach equals a healthy llama.

Digestive Disorders in Llamas

Digestive disorders are diseases or disorders associated with the digestive tract, also called *gastrointestinal* disorders. The clinical signs are anorexia, abdominal distension, depression, increased pulse, subnormal temperature, and colic.

However, these signs are not diagnostic, so additional tests should be done to confirm. Some gastrointestinal disorders are explained below.

Mega-esophagus

Mega-esophagus is a digestive disorder in which the esophagus dilates (gets larger) and loses motility (the ability to move food into the stomach). When this happens, food substances accumulate in the esophagus and have difficulty moving on to the stomach.

Dilatation of the esophagus is relatively common in llamas, especially after instances of choking. Common signs of mega-esophagus are chronic weight loss and postprandial regurgitation of food. The exact cause of this disorder is unknown and there is no treatment. Some animals can maintain the condition for an extended period, while others will continue to lose weight.

Stomach Atony

Stomach atony is a rare gastrointestinal disorder in llamas, and the cause of this disorder is unknown. Common signs are reduced or complete cessation of food consumption, depression, and loss of body condition. Other gastrointestinal problems, like diarrhea, may also occur. Fluid consumption is one way to correct this disorder.

Ulcers

Ulcers in llamas develop in the third compartment because of the stomach acid present there. Common signs are decreased food consumption, depression, and intermittent to severe colic and stress is also a significant factor. No particular treatment is recommended, but is usually based on clinical signs and history. Administration of omeprazole can help reduce acid production. Stress reduction, parenteral antibiotics, and other supportive therapy can aid the recovery process.

Hepatic Disease

Hepatic disease is a relatively common problem in llamas. It can be caused by stress or abrupt change in the diet or feed. Common signs are diminished growth, ill thrift (when their growth rate is slower than expected) and acute death. Treatment is usually based on specific symptoms, but increased serum bile acids and enzyme concentrations can aid the recovery process. The mortality rate in untreated animals is relatively high, so if you notice the signs, you must give them the appropriate treatment.

Diarrhea

This gastrointestinal disorder is not common in llamas. The primary causes of diarrhea include cryptosporidium, rotavirus, coronavirus, and enteropathogenic strains of Escherichia coli. Some crias (baby llamas) may also experience transitory diarrhea 2–3 weeks after birth, but diarrhea in older llamas is usually caused by infection or associated with a change in feed.

Constipation and Indigestion

Clinical treatment is recommended for this gastrointestinal disorder and diet modification. In young llamas, bladder rupture, retained meconium, and clostridial enterotoxemia should be considered.

Bloat

Bloat is a gastrointestinal condition of hyperacidity from grain overload, traumatic reticuloperitonitis and abomasal displacement. This gastrointestinal disorder is not common in llamas.

Prevention and Treatment Therapy for Gastrointestinal Disorders in Llamas

The treatment for gastrointestinal disorders in llamas is similar to that of domestic ruminants. However, when signs of acute abdomen disorders are observed, it should be treated as an emergency condition requiring immediate care.

With ulcers, transplantation of the stomach contents from another llama or cow can be helpful. Using mineral oil, vinegar and bicarbonate can also help, especially when the atony is related to grain overload.

Most of the gastrointestinal disorders are caused by their diet. Llamas should be fed mostly legume pastures and mixed grasses. You can also add a concentrate supplementation if your llama requires a lot of energy, especially pregnant/lactating and packing llamas.

Nutritional Requirements for Llamas

You must know the llama's nutritional requirement as it is essential to raising a healthy producing herd. The dietary requirements will affect their reproduction, the health of their crias (baby llama), heat stress, wool quality, and milk production.

The nutritional requirement may vary slightly depending on what purpose your llamas are serving, your location, and the pasture you provide for them. But generally, the llama's diet should consist of fiber, protein, salt, calcium, phosphorus, minerals, and vitamins.

Fiber and Energy

The major sources of energy in their diet are pastures and hay. Good leafy grass hay that is not dusty or moldy will provide the fiber and energy required. A grain like corn is also a high-energy source, and it can be added to their diet to help them get the energy they need to stay strong and healthy.

However, it should be added in the right proportion. Llamas in late gestation or early lactation can have 3/4 lb. of cracked corn added to their diet to give them the energy they require. Cracked corn can be added to the expectant mother's diet about four to six weeks before the delivery date.

You can also continue the feeding it after birth, especially if the mother loses a lot of weight after giving birth. She will also require higher energy, as she will be feeding her cria.

You should, however, note that grains like oats or corn should be used only as supplemental high-energy sources and not as the primary energy source in their diet. Grains should also not be given in extremely hot weather conditions.

Protein

The protein requirement for llamas is relatively low. Usually, good leafy grass hay will provide the required protein intake for your llama. However, where protein supplement is necessary (lactation or cold weather), you can add 50% alfalfa hay to their diet. However, it must only be fed as a supplement, not as their main feed because of the high level of protein in it. Alfalfa hay is the most likely culprit for fat pads in the mammary tissue, and it negatively affects the crias by adding excess fat during their primary growing season.

Also, excess calcium obtained from alfalfa hay will upset the Calcium (Ca) – Phosphorus (P) balance, which is vital for the rapid growth of your crias. The deficiencies and imbalance of calcium and phosphorous can cause abnormal bone growth formation, like bowed legs. This happens when the mother or crias eats too much alfalfa.

Be careful with the amount of protein you feed your llamas. A 6-10 percent protein content is recommended, though crias may have a higher requirement of about 16 percent. The quality of the pasture and the protein content is higher in the spring when plants are growing actively.

Salt, Vitamins, Calcium, and Phosphorus

Salt, vitamins, calcium, and phosphorus are also a good supplement (feed). These nutrients are essential for their wellbeing, but you must regulate how these supplements are fed, ensuring they are administered evenly.

The most efficient way to feed and control their dietary needs is by providing them the supplement by way of a pellet only. Mixing the minerals and vitamins as powders, loose grains, and pellets do not allow for a controllable and consistent diet.

The ingredients will not be evenly distributed, as most of it will fall to the bottom of the bag. Keep the pellet size at about 1/8 inches to prevent choking. If your llama chokes while feeding on the pellet, stop feeding it for a couple of days. You can then slowly introduce the pellet back into its feed.

The supplement usually contains all the vitamins, minerals, and salt. However, you need also to give them a loose trace mineral mix as the absence of a trace mineral like selenium in their diet can cause problems. Your animals might experience weak crias, growth problems, white muscle disease, lactation, and even reproduction issues.

Check the selenium level of your animals at random when you take their blood for a periodic checkup. If the selenium level is above 150 to 200, it is normal. However, anything below 150 is cause for concern.

Llamas also need a lot of Vitamin E in their diet. The Vitamin E in dried forages is not sufficient so give them supplements; lack of or insufficiency of Vitamin E in llamas shows up as crooked legs and the development of weak crias.

Ensure you feed them a balanced diet in hot, humid weather as it will help them fight the heat stress. You might also have to up the dosage of supplements when your animals are in late gestation, early lactation, and in freezing weather.

While understanding the nutrition of llamas can be complicated and a bit confusing, it is essential knowledge to breed a healthy and strong herd. They can eat different feeds without you watching them and still appear to do fine. However, the problems will eventually show up. It can be in birthing problems, costly veterinarian bills for sicknesses – or even death.

Provide routine checkups to monitor the health of your animals. Perform their blood tests regularly and randomly check the llama's selenium level. Checkups should include calcium and phosphorus balance tests, and protein levels with a CBC.

Occasionally, you can do an IgG (immunoglobulin) blood test to see what their zinc and copper levels are. Also weigh them periodically and keep a record to ensure you know their overall health and wellbeing.

Feeding Recommendation for Llamas

Llamas are adaptive feeders, eating grasses, shrubs, forbs (herbaceous broadleaf vegetation, non-woody) and trees. They are herbivores, grazers and browsers. They need fiber, energy, vitamins and protein to remain healthy and they receive energy and fiber by eating hay, corn, pasture and oats.

For protein sources, you can feed them alfalfa hay, grass hay, and geldings. Llamas also have a high requirement for vitamin C, which can be obtained from pellets or powder. Also, water always needs to be available.

Alfalfa hay is a good choice of hay. However, avoid using it all time for feed, complementing it with mixed pastures like grass and legumes. You can also supplement their diet with grain or concentrates if they will be used as pack animals.

An adult llama will consume about 2 percent of its body weight per day. That can increase to 3 percent if they are packing, pulling carriages or any other activity, or to 4 percent if it's pregnant or lactating. On average, llamas require about one bale of hay a week or a pound of hay a day.

You can feed approximately three to five llamas per acre depending on the quality of the pasture. You can also practice rotational grazing of llamas to help utilize the pasture to a greater extent. Using fields to meet most of their nutritional requirements is cost effective because pasture is less costly than purchasing supplemental hay or grains.

An essential factor in the feeding and diet is regularity and consistency. The suggested daily feeding proportions are 1 lb. supplements (grain), 5 lbs. from pasture and hay, plus some free trace minerals.

Things to Avoid Feeding Your Llamas

1. Cantharidins (Blister Beetle Poison)

Cantharidin is a toxic terpenoid substance secreted by blister beetles and can harm or kill your herd, and with only a tiny quantity ingested, your animal will be in danger. Llamas can ingest cantharidin in alfalfa hay infested by blister beetles.

Therefore, inspect the alfalfa hay thoroughly before you feed it to them. When the alfalfa hay has an oily-looking substance, then it's likely that blister beetles have infested it. Do not feed that hay to them.

Llamas that have eaten a large amount of this toxin will show signs of shock, and, unfortunately, die within hours. Symptoms of cantharidin poisoning are depression, elevated temperature, diarrhea, frequent urination and increased pulse.

If you think they have eaten cantharidin, contact the veterinarian immediately. If the antidote is given to the animal immediately, maybe it will survive. However, if the animal has eaten a large amount, it may not survive.

2. High Copper Content Feeds

A high copper content can be harmful to your llama, and some studies show that feeds with high copper content can cause spontaneous abortion. Feeds such as cow minerals, pig minerals, or chicken food may lead to copper toxicity. When your animal has copper toxicity, it will have copper-colored urine and a sweet smell.

3. Too Many Grains

You should not give them too many grains, as it can lead to grain overload or poisoning. This results from the carbohydrates fermenting in the animal's stomach instead of getting digested. Lactic acid is produced, which causes dehydration and slowing of the gut – sometimes death.

Barley and wheat are the biggest causes of grain overload, along with excess oats and lupins. Also, a sudden switch of your llama's diet to grain can cause grain overload; therefore, regularity and consistency are essential with their nutrition and feeding.

4. Feed with a High Level of Protein Content

High protein content in their diet can lead to complications, primarily adding fat to the mammary pads and obesity. Plus, crias ingesting too much protein will gain excessive weight quickly, which is detrimental to their health. In breeding females obesity can add to heat stress, a lack of milk production and dystocia, which is otherwise defined as a "difficult birth."

5. Sweet Feed

Avoid feeding them sweet feeds as high amounts of sugar and starch can cause digestive upsets like acidosis and bloat.

Chapter 7: Llama Health and Disease Prevention

Quick Fact - *A llama is a hardy animal and can easily navigate harsh environments. They are sure-footed and can traverse difficult terrain at high altitudes. However, although they make great pack animals, they do know their limits. Try to put too much weight on a llama and it will simply refuse to move or lie down.*

As hardy as they are, llamas and alpacas get sick and their diseases can be difficult to spot. While some conditions are easy to recognize, many others are not detectable until they are severely ill. Often, a sick animal behaves just like a healthy one.

Unlike you, your llama or alpaca cannot talk. Even if they are in pain, they cannot communicate their displeasure to you in words. To identify changes in their normal behavior, you must be observant and understand the animal's normal behavior so you can spot anything outside of the ordinary.

In this chapter, we will examine diseases that affect lamas and alpacas. We also will look at ways to prevent them from getting sick.

Dangerous Diseases that Affect Llamas and Alpacas

You have probably heard about communicable and non-communicable diseases, and we'll be looking briefly at both.

But first, what causes diseases? A lot of things can make an animal sick. Animals are comprised of chemical and biological systems, and in a healthy animal there's a balance between these systems. An animal becomes ill when this delicate balance is disturbed. In other instances, the cause of the disease is genetic.

But diseases can be caused by the intake of chemicals (or drugs) that act as a toxic agent to tip the delicate balance of health.

In genetic and chemical causes, the disease is noncommunicable, meaning that it cannot be transferred to another animal.

Other times, the animal's body is invaded by a virus, parasite, fungi or bacteria; living things that feed off your animal and disturb the internal balance. These can live on the inside or the outside of the body; either way, they can cause serious problems.

These living invaders often multiply on their host and release harmful secretions, and sometimes sick animals can pass these living organisms to other animals. These diseases are called communicable infectious diseases.

The following are diseases that affect llamas and alpacas.

Anemia

Anemia is causes the skin to become pale and is easily spotted by checking the animal's lower eyelid to see what color the membrane is.

It should be bright pink in a healthy animal, while anemic animals eyelids will be close to white. Their coat will look dull or shabby, they will be tired and weak and may have a poor appetite.

Anemia is more of a symptom than it is a disease. It happens when there is a reduction in the number of red blood cells which can occur because of severe parasitic infestation on the animal's skin, including fleas, lice, ticks, and other similar parasites. Internal parasites, such as worms, can also cause anemia.

In addition, anemia can be caused by severe blood loss from an injury or childbirth or by feeding llamas a poor diet, specifically a diet lacking in the trace amounts of copper they require.

Treating anemia can be easy, depending on the cause and severity of the illness. In the early stages, consider changing their diet to one rich in protein, which helps rebuild the red blood cells. Also give them iron supplements, vitamins, minerals, and probiotics.

In severe cases, the animal might need a blood transfusion and left untreated, anemia can lead to death. Whatever the case, if you notice any of these signs, contact your vet immediately.

Bottle Jaw

This is a caused by severe case of anemia, evidenced by a pronounced swelling in the lower jaw. The barber pole worm is one of the most common causes of bottle jaw. This deadly condition requires immediate veterinary attention when the symptoms are noticed.

Anaplasmosis

This disease happens when the red blood cells of your llama or alpaca are infected. The condition is rare, non-communicable and is transmitted by insects, such as ticks and flies, depositing a parasite into the animal's blood.

Since this disease is an infection of the blood, the first sign to look out for is anemia. The animal will seem weak and pale, and your animal will have a fever. The mucus membranes of the nose and mouth will also turn yellow.

As the infection becomes severe, the animal will reject its food and, along with dehydration, you will notice severe weight loss.

Anaplasmosis is a dangerous disease in llamas and alpacas. Even though there are treatments for the disease, it weakens the animal, leaving it with a defective immune system and weak stamina. If you notice any of the above signs, contact your veterinarian immediately.

Barber Pole

The barber pole worm is one of the most dreadful worms that can affect llama or alpaca. The worm stays in their stomach, piercing the walls of the stomach and sucking out the blood.

The blood-sucking process quickly leads to anemia and can be dangerous. Signs of the disease at the initial stage are pale eyes, weight loss, and tiredness.

Subsequently, you will notice bottle jaw (an area of edema under the chin), or the animal may collapse. If diagnosed early enough, the barber pole worm can be treated by veterinarians. As a preventive tip, make sure you deworm your animals regularly.

Coccidiosis

Coccidiosis is caused by a microscopic parasite called Coccidia. This parasite lives in the cells of the animal, causing damage in the small intestine.

Younger llamas and alpacas have a higher risk of infection; however, adult llamas and alpacas can get infected but gain immunity from the infections.

This disease is common with animals kept in non-sanitary conditions. Stress and overcrowding can also make animals vulnerable. It is very contagious, so infected animals must be isolated from the herd.

At the start of the illness, you will notice mucus-filled diarrhea. If unattended, the stool becomes bloody, potentially leading to dehydration, weight loss, anemia and stunted growth.

While the condition is treatable, prevention is usually best. You can always prevent the disease by keeping the animal's environment clean and not housing too many together.

You can also take fecal samples to a vet's clinic to check for dangerous parasites.

Foot Rot

Foot Rot is a common livestock disease, not just in llamas and alpacas. It is a bacterial infection that affects their feet.

The leading cause of this disease is zinc deficiency, but it can also occur when the animal is kept in muddy wet conditions for too long.

It starts with swelling between the toes of the animal, and you may see lumps on the pads of their feet. They will likely walk with a limp because the swelling is usually painful.

When the condition is left unattended, their feet decay gradually, producing creamy fluids with a foul odor, leading to nerve and tissue damage in the affected foot.

You can treat foot rot at the initial stage by cleaning the affected area and removing the rotten parts. Once the area is thoroughly cleaned, apply iodine and antibiotics.

Luckily, the infection in llamas and alpacas is not as severe as sheep and goats since they have toes instead of hooves. However, care must still be taken because it is contagious, especially in the first seven days.

If you spot the above signs, contact your vet.

White Muscle Disease

This disease is common to sheep, llamas, and alpacas and occurs when they consume a diet poor in vitamin E, selenium, or both.

The disease can affect the animal's muscles, heart muscles, or both.

When it affects the heart muscles, you will notice the animal struggling to breathe and you may see blood or mucus leaking from the nose.

If it affects their muscles, they will look arched and their back will seem stiff and hunched over. The disease leaves the animals with a weakened immune system.

Both vitamin E and selenium deficiency are common in animals that graze. Vitamin E deficiency develops when the animal ingests grass low in vitamin E, whereas a selenium deficiency occurs when the animal feeds from soil lacking the mineral.

While treating a deficiency is easy, white muscle disease must be treated by a vet. If you suspect a deficiency in your animals, give them supplements, but if you suspect white muscle disease, talk to your veterinarian.

Urolithiasis

We've all heard of kidney stones; some of us have been unlucky enough to have them. Llamas and alpacas can also get these blockages in the urinary path, usually when there is an imbalance of phosphorus and calcium in their diet. These minerals will then form solid crystals that will block the path of urine.

The disease is common in males, especially when fed a grain-heavy diet. It can also happen when they consume too much alfalfa.

Animals with this disease are easy to spot as they do not urinate often. When they do urinate, they will appear to be in distress, and sometimes the urine will come out in a trickle instead of a strong flow. The animal might also not want to walk or will walk stiffly or stand with their hind legs stretched out.

The condition is serious, as death can occur in a few hours. If you notice these signs, call your vet immediately.

Generally, it kidney stones occur more often in sheep than in llamas and alpacas. In the same vein, it happens more in male llamas and alpacas than it does in females.

On a general note, you can prevent the disease by letting animals graze on their own so they can select healthy foods. Alternatively, you can feed them with forage products.

Care must be taken when giving llamas concentrate foods – foods rich in protein and carbohydrates like grains, legumes, and so on – as this can quickly tip the mineral balance in their body.

Arthritis

Yes, you read that correctly! They can also have arthritis, and while many things can cause this, the fundamental cause is aging. Other causes of arthritis in llamas include malnutrition, infection, tight confinement, and injuries.

Just like in humans, arthritis in llamas and alpacas is not a transmittable disease. Animals with arthritis will have limited movement due to pain, and you might notice them lying down often. They might also lose weight, develop swollen joints, and dull coats.

Treating arthritis is usually done by treating the root cause. Therefore, if you suspect that your animal has this disease, you must seek the advice of a veterinarian.

Pink Eye

There are two types of pink eye disease in alpacas and llamas: infectious and noninfectious. The infectious type is caused by viruses or bacteria and transmitted between animals via flying insects.

The non-infectious type usually results from vitamin A deficiency, stings from insects, scratches, or toxins.

Depending on the cause, pink eye can be a severe problem. The infectious type initially appears as red, swollen eyes with discharge and, then you will notice the transparent covering of the eyes becoming thick and visible. If not treated early, the animal can become blind and in worse cases, the infection can spread to the animal's brain, leading to death.

The moment you spot pink eye in any of your animals, segregate the animals immediately, protecting the sick llama and preventing the spread of the infection to the rest of the herd.

The non-infectious type can be treated easily using eye ointments. However, to be sure, consult a veterinarian for a proper checkup to determine the cause.

Sore Mouth

This disease is caused by a virus closely related to chickenpox. Just as in human chickenpox, this disease is contagious in llamas and alpacas. The condition usually penetrates the skin via cuts in the skin.

Young llamas can contact the disease while their mothers are nursing them and it is dangerous to the younger animals; not only will the disease pass on to them, they won't be able to feed properly.

The disease usually runs its course within 3 - 4 weeks. During this period, blisters will develop around the animal's less hairy body parts, such as the lips and inside the mouth. With time, these small blisters become bigger as they turn into scabs.

When you spot these signs, separate the sick animals from the healthy. Your vet will prescribe ointments you can apply to the affected parts. Take your time and clean out everywhere the animal has been before you separated it and treat the sores, so they do not get infected with bacteria.

Just like in humans, a survivor becomes immune to the disease. While this is good news, it calls for caution. The survivors, although immune, can still carry the disease and transfer it to other animals.

There is no known cure for this infection. The animal is managed while the disease runs its course.

Health Care Practices for Disease Prevention in Llamas and Alpacas

Their health is non-negotiable; they depend on you to help keep them safe healthy.

Four factors contribute to disease in any animal: lack of immunity, disease-causing organisms, environment, and stress.

An animal whose immunity is not compromised is unlikely to become sick, or at least not seriously. The same applies to animals that do not come into contact with a disease-causing organism, but the right environment will protect them and reduce the risk of disease.

Stress refers to conditions that can make an animal predisposed to illness. They include injuries, malnutrition, inappropriate use of medication, and so on.

For an animal to remain healthy, all these factors must be kept in check. Here are a few tips to help you do that:

1. Understand your Animal

You must first understand what normal behavior is *to be able* to spot abnormal behavior. Notice that your animals are unique individuals and will behave differently. For example, alpacas are shy animals and might not be as active as llamas. It would, therefore, be wrong to judge both animals on the same scale for activity.

Even among alpacas, you will have some friendly animals and some that don't mingle so well. The idea is for you to understand each one of them by observing and learning their usual behavior.

Every morning, before you feed your llamas, check on them, looking for animals not responding well. While feeding, look out for those that won't eat or appear to be less interested in eating, and check for animals that isolate themselves from the herd.

Animals with excessive salivation, discharge from the nose, bloody stool, diarrhea, or teary eyes require immediate attention. If you spot sick animals, remove them from the herd immediately to avoid the spread of any potential disease.

2. Restrict Human Contact

Humans are one of the biggest carriers of animal diseases. If you own a llama or alpaca farm, always restrict how often people access your farmland and your farm animals, including the vet.

If it's a must that you have visitors, find a system for disinfecting them before they enter your farm. You can make use of foot dips made of water and a strong disinfectant placed at the entrance to your property and have disinfectant hand washes ready too.

If you have a sick animal, take it to the vet or have the vet visit your premises as soon as possible; make sure they see the animal separately from the rest of the herd.

3. Proper Feeding Is Important

Llamas need to eat well, not just the right amount of food but the proper quality of food too.

The best way to feed llamas and alpacas is to let them graze and select their own food. Where that is impossible, you must provide food of the highest quality, balanced and containing all the essential nutrients. It should be clean and presented in clean bowls, and your llamas and alpacas should also have access to clean water at all times.

4. Vaccines and Other Medications

Ensure your animals are given all the necessary vaccinations and keep in touch with your vet to make sure any boosters or yearly vaccines are given at the correct time.

As crucial as vaccines are, regular deworming is just as important. Speak with your vet to arrange a deworming schedule.

Also, give your animals multivitamins that will boost their immune systems, keep them active and reduce stress.

5. Keep an Ideal Environment

The ideal environment for your llamas and alpacas is clean, uncrowded, and kept at a comfortable temperature. This will eliminate or at least significantly reduce the risk of potentially dangerous disease-causing organisms.

You should have no more than seven alpacas or four llamas on one acre of land, and you will need a barn or shed to ensure they can escape harsh weather. Last, your llamas should be sheared at the correct time to ensure they do not overheat or suffer from the cold.

Chapter 8: Llama Breeding and Cria Birthing

Quick Fact - *Baby llamas are called crias, a Spanish word that translates to "baby". Female llamas usually have just one cria at a time; twins are possible, but very rare. A llama pregnancy lasts for around 350 days and a cria will weigh 20 to 30 pounds when born.*

Llama/Alpaca Reproductive System

The species of llamas and alpacas today originate from South America and share a common feral ancestry. Their reproductive systems are similar but distinct.

Female

The female llama or alpaca ovary is not so different from that of a mare, but it resembles a cow. Relative to body size, the reproductive tract is small when the llama or alpaca is not pregnant.

The ovum is small and cannot be detected clearly by ultrasound instruments, at least not the ones we have today. However, antra follicles can be detected, which are small, measuring about 1 to 2 mm in diameter. Several fluid-filled follicles are also present.

Between 10 to 12 months after birth, ovarian activities will begin in the llama or alpaca. Ovarian follicles assume a peripheral cortex arrangement, and any area on the surface of the ovary can accommodate ovulation. Corpus luteum (CL) and large follicles in llamas and alpacas are visible and palpable. Corpus luteum is a bundle of cells formed in the llama's ovary and is what produces the progesterone hormone in the early stages of pregnancy.

Male

Relative to their body sizes, the llama and alpaca have relatively small testes. The llama's testes usually measure at least 3 X 6 cm at birth, while the alpacas' testes are usually at least 2 X 4 cm. The testes are typically close to the body of the animal and the prepuce (sheath) adheres to the penis in young males, not detaching until around 2 to 3 years of age. An unstimulated prepuce not stimulated is usually caudo-dorsally directed; it points towards the back of the tail, which explains why they appear to urinate backwards. Compared to other livestock species, the llama and alpaca testes are small.

The penis points forward. The prepuce is attached to the penis. When the animal reaches 1- 1/2 to 2 – or even three – years old, the penis will detach.

Not all the animals will reach sexual maturity at the same time. Most males breed at 18 to 24 months old while some may become fully sexually mature when they reach 30 months. Generally, a llama may attain sexual maturity and become fertile earlier than the alpaca.

The cranial, lateral, and caudal preputial muscles in the sheath aid erection. They also have roles to play when the animal displays mating behaviors.

Llamas and alpacas usually have a low quantity of semen, making it very difficult to evaluate. This is a common problem in the camelid family.

The ejaculations of fertile males are inconsistent. Some people resort to training their animals to mount on a dummy, preparing it with an artificial vagina to give the male the feel of climbing a real female.

Usually, they sedate the animals, and they may introduce electro-ejaculation, although this isn't always efficient. Another option is to collect the semen from the vagina of the female after mating.

Llama/Alpaca Reproduction

Reproduction in llamas and alpacas begins at puberty. The female llama and alpaca attain sexual maturity between 10 to 18 months of age and can begin breeding. However, following a veterinarian's advice, some people do not let their female llamas and alpacas breed until they weigh up to 90 kg (200 pounds) for llamas and 40 kg (90 pounds) for alpacas.

Alternatively, they can breed when they weigh two-thirds of their mature body weight. This precaution is taken because of the relatively small size of the female alpaca and llama and it also helps to avoid challenges associated with early breeding, such as dystocia.

When puberty begins, the animal experiences follicular waves, developing a follicle in the interval of 12 to 14 days. The male llama and alpacas breed between 18 to 24 months of age, and by that time, the penis is no longer attached to the sheath and the testes will have grown significantly.

Ovulation in the female llama and alpaca occur when it has been mated because they are induced ovulators. Before mating can occur, the receptive female will assume a position that allows the male access into her and, while the male is mounting her, he will start "orgling," the sound they make while mating. The common belief is this sound will help the female ovulate.

Ejaculation lasts for between 5 and 45 minutes, although the average is about 20 minutes, accruing to a relatively small volume of 2 to 5 ml. After mating for 24 to 30 hours, the semen can still induce reflex ovulation.

A pregnant llama or alpaca will not be receptive and will reject the male's advances. After 2 to 3 days of ovulation, there will be a CL (corpus luteum). Then, about seven days after mating, the fertilized oocyte will be present in the uterus.

There will be implantation by 30 days into the gestation period. A hyperechoic embryo will be there to show that the llama is pregnant 21 days into gestation, and at 45 days into the gestation period – perhaps a bit more – you can perform rectal palpation to know if the llama is pregnant. For alpacas, it will be difficult given their size, but if the person has relatively small hands, palpation may be possible. This is best left to a veterinary doctor, though.

The gestation period for llamas is around 345 to 350 days. Usually the dams deliver one cria, although sometimes they deliver twins – but this is rare.

Reproductive Problems and Management

Like other animals, llamas and alpacas face some challenges with their reproductive systems. In males, these problems may include:

• **Acute Scrotal Swelling**

This problem can be caused by heat stress, infection, trauma, and so on. There can also be penile swelling from injury to the penis and urolithiasis.

Symptoms of penile swelling can obstruction of the free flow of urine. Depending on the extent of swelling and injury, surgery, flushing, and cystotomy may be recommended.

If surgery is the option, you have a significant role to play afterward. The animal will need extra care to recuperate fully, while therapies and drugs should be provided.

- **Heat Stress**

This problem affects the llama or alpaca's penis and animals suffering from a penile injury may present with hydrocele (scrotal swelling) and experience scrotal edema.

The effect of heat stress can cause the animal to become uninterested in mounting the female. They may experience reduced fertility for, lasting up to two months or more, even years and sometimes, the animal can become permanently infertile.

When the case is severe, the animal may become depressed and have a muscular weakness while other symptoms are excess salivation, dehydration, etc.

There are several ways you can protect them against heat stress; the most obvious is by providing shade. Animals should not be in the sun for long periods of time, and if a male has been exposed to the sun for an extended period, he should be cooled immediately, until he regains normal body temperature.

When the animal is dehydrated, he should be rehydrated. Don't allow him to gulp huge amounts of water as this can lead to problems such as a diluted sodium level in the blood which can cause weakness and even convulsions in the worst case. Shearing is also recommended. If the condition is severe. Take the animal to the veterinary clinic for proper care, and when necessary, the veterinarian may have to administer medication. In times like this, you should not subject the animal to a long, rough transport. This situation may require a house call from the veterinarian.

- **Testicular Hypoplasia**

Another reproductive problem that male llamas and alpacas can have is testicular hypoplasia, caused by a bridge in the sexual development of the animal. This causes the size of the testes to be disproportionate to the size of his body. The testes do not develop as they should and become smaller than they should be for the age of the animal.

Sometimes, this situation can be caused by poor nutrition, like zinc deficiency. It can also be an effect of cytogenetic and endocrine abnormalities or may occur where the germ cells are insufficient.

Hypoplasia of the testes results from irregular progressive sclerosis and degeneration. It usually becomes glaringly obvious after puberty, but when both testes are of equal size, it's difficult to recognize.

If one of the testes is smaller than the other, it's called *unilateral hypoplasia.* It will be easy to detect because you can compare the contralateral testis.

If the situation is not complicated, the animal may just have low sperm morphology. However, in extreme cases, he may be aspermic.

There are preventive measures you can adopt to avoid this situation. Be careful not to allow breeding between affected animals because if the cause is genetic, it may be transferred to the cria.

Castration is another viable treatment option. Also, you may want to slaughter the animal for its carcass value.

Female llamas are more likely to have issues because their reproductive system is more complex than males. Some of the most common issues are:

• Dystocia

One challenge llamas and alpacas may have during delivery is dystocia (difficulty in giving birth.)

Dystocia can occur because of several factors.

If your dam is having dystocia, there will be signs. Usually, with delivery, you must be vigilant. Any slight inconsistency should be checked. If there is a delay at any stage, be concerned.

All may not be well if the dam remains in the first stage of labor more than is reasonably expected. If she spends up to four hours or more in the first stage, there may be a problem. Also, if the fetus is visible, but the dam has not delivered it for up to 30 minutes or more, there is definitely a problem.

- **Uterine Torsion**

Uterine torsion is another problem that may cause a difficult a delivery. This situation is where the uterine is twisted; the delivery may not progress from the first stage to the second. This condition typically occurs in the last month of the pregnancy when the dam is exhausted.

In the second stage of delivery, there may be a delay if the fetus assumes the wrong position. It can also happen if the birth canal is not patent enough (sufficiently opened) to allow the fetus through. Sometimes, the fetus is larger than the birth canal. This problem is one reason why some people do not crossbreed llama and alpaca. Llamas are usually bigger than alpacas. When there is crossbreeding, the fetus may be too big for the alpaca to deliver.

Situations where the fetus assumes the wrong position is common among camelids. This problem should be corrected before delivery and can be fixed manually or spontaneously. Without this correction, the dam may not have a normal birth.

You will know if your dam has uterine torsion when it displays symptoms such as depression and colic (abdominal pain.) You will know if the dam has colic if she kicks at her abdomen.

A veterinarian should check on the llama or alpaca to know how twisted the uterus is. He/she will note the direction in which it is twisted and resolve it. Resolution may involve medicating the dam to calm her down so the process will succeed.

The dam assumes a position of lateral recumbency. The dam will be held in place, and the process will be performed. The uterus and fetus will be held in a static position. It can be done with hands or by placing a plank on the dam's abdomen. After this, the dam will be rotated to the direction opposite which the uterine is twisted; this process can be repeated depending on how twisted the uterine is.

If this procedure is done up to three times, and the situation is not resolved, the dam must undergo surgery.

Cria Birthing

Cria birthing is the delivery of a newborn.

Labor Signs

Labor signs may begin earlier in some dams than others. Therefore, monitor the llama or alpaca when it is about 330 days into gestation. At this stage, check on it often – every few hours – which enables you to know when labor is approaching.

Llamas and alpacas do not necessarily experience labor in the same way, but some signs are common among them. These signs are:

• Fuller Udder

The llama or alpaca's udder will become fuller as the day of delivery draws near. Two to three weeks before birth, the milk will start to flow. And by 3 to 4 days before delivery, the teats will have a telltale sign of being waxy.

• Vulva Size

A few days before delivery, the vulva will increase in size, swelling and becoming more pronounced.

• Restlessness

One common sign of labor among most animals, including llamas and alpacas, is restlessness. The dam may move, shift, or hum, she may roll about, lying down and rising again, and so on. Sometimes, she will lose her appetite and refuse to eat, but will instead chew her cud.

• Unusual Behavior

When delivery is near, the llama or alpaca will display unusual behaviors. Anything the dam does not do before pregnancy; she may do now. If you notice any behavior out of the ordinary, it is likely a sign of labor.

Stages of Labor

Before delivery, the llama will go into labor. There are three stages of labor.

- **Stage 1**

During this period, the animal will urinate frequently. She will separate herself from the herd, make a humming sound continuously. These behaviors will persist throughout the first stage of labor.

At this stage, the uterus contracts and the cervix dilate. The cervix assumes the same width as the vagina, and the fetus moves into the pelvic inlet. This stage can last from 1 to 6 hours.

- **Stage 2**

This stage begins from the rupturing of the membrane to the birth of the cria. It takes 30 minutes or more. You may see the female lying down and standing up continuously, the abdomen is strained, and the water bag or amniotic sac may be visible at the vulva; you may even see it rupture. The female will obviously have contractions and the contractions be close together in time. If you see her resting between contractions and you think that things are going too slowly, don't panic at this stage – she is getting tired by the contractions and wants to rest.

- **Stage 3**

This stage lasts for four hours or more – up to six and is the stage where the placenta is passed. Know, unlike many other species, the mother does not ingest the placenta and typically will not lick the newborn cria, either. Examine the placenta and make sure it is intact, filled with fluid and has no tears in it. Dispose of it carefully, wearing gloves (do NOT use bare hands) as it can attract nearby predators.

These stages of labor usually last longer in first-time deliveries.

When to Get Veterinary Help

Call for veterinary assistance when:

● Stage 1 goes past 5 hours and there are no signs of contractions.

● Stage 2 goes past 30 minutes and the birth is showing no signs of progression.

● Stage 3 - if the placenta has not been passed within 8 hours after the birth or, if the dam gives birth at night, by the next morning.

Cria Birthing

Cria birthing occurs in the second stage of labor, and the placenta follows within a few hours. Before the birthing begins, get a birthing kit, which should include:

1. Flashlight or torch

If the llama or alpaca gives birth late in the day, which is unusual, as most give birth between 8 am and noon, you may need light to see what's happening and you will need to note the time of delivery.

2. Towels

You will cover the bedding with clean towels during the birth, and when the new cria arrives, you will need the towels to dry it off and clean the birthing fluids.

3. Scissors and dental floss

You will need these to cut and tie the umbilical cord.

4. Iodine and bottle

This is used for dipping the end of the umbilical cord. Use an empty pill bottle and a 7% iodine tincture.

5. Betadine surgical scrub and sterile lubrication

You will need it to sterilize your hands and birthing supplies, especially if you need to assist the veterinarian.

6. Rectal thermometer

It is used for checking the newborn crias temperature, especially if he or she seems to be lethargic or weak.

7. Sterile lubrication

Just in case you need to help the llama with the birth.

8. Feeding bottle and nipple

If the cria cannot nurse immediately, you will need to feed it.

9. Supplement

If the cria cannot nurse immediately after birth, a multi-species colostrum supplement must be given – this is critical.

10. Milk replacer

A multi-species milk replacer is given where the cria cannot nurse properly – choose one with a minimum 24% protein.

11. Electrolytes

It is used to rehydrate the dam and reverse the effect of fluid loss in the cria after delivery.

12. Disposable bags

These are used to dispose of the afterbirth, soiled towels, and other things you need to throw away.

Newborn llama cria weigh between 20 to 30 pounds at birth, and they are usually larger than alpaca cria, which typically weigh between 15 to 20 pounds at birth.

How to Care for a Newborn Cria

Caring for your newborn cria begins before the cria is birthed. The period of waiting for your newborn cria is packed with several emotions, so you need all the tips you can get!

Naturally, some things will go as they are meant to. However, you have a role to play. Knowing what to do and how to do them will help you better handle whatever situation may arise. Some ways you can better care for the newborn cria include:

- **Preparing for a Smooth Birth**

If the birth is not smooth, the newborn cria may not do well. Before the due date for delivery, ensure that the llama or alpaca has a clean and appropriate place to deliver. A leveled grassy area will do fine in good weather, but the site should be safe. There should be no sharp objects or unneeded items to clutter the area.

If the weather is not favorable, the llama or alpaca should be delivered in a clean, well ventilated stall and have comfortable bedding.

Prepare the birthing kit and have it readily available for when you need it. Make sure it contains all the items listed above.

- **Immediately After Birth**

When the cria is born, check it is healthy. The dam should be in a clean, warm, room - weather permitting.

Ensure the cria is breathing properly. Sometimes, the cria has difficulty breathing because the nose or mouth is blocked, so make sure you clean all the birthing fluid off its face, paying particular but gentle attention to the eyes, nose and mouth.

Check if the cria's temperature is okay - it should be 35 C or 95º F. If it is less, the cria is too cold and must be warmed up.

One hour after birth, the cria should be able to stand. Two hours after birth, it should be able to nurse, but if these do not happen, you can assist it.

If you try, but nothing happens, contact the veterinary doctor.

- **Medical Care**

Although the medical care for the cria begins before birth, it is necessary during and after birth.

Routine medical checkups for both the cria and dam are necessary. Crias born between October and March should be given a vitamin D supplement, as they are unlikely to be out in the sunlight to receive it naturally.

Vaccinate the cria for Tetanus and Clostridium Type C and D, and vaccinate against diseases they are prone to contracting. You will need to check with your veterinarian what diseases are common in your region.

Your veterinarian can guide you against harmful practices and advise you on the right steps to take to care for your new herd member.

Don't be scared when you have a pregnant llama; with the proper preparation, you can help your llama during pregnancy and the birthing process.

The First Few Days – Feeding

The most critical time for your newborn cria is the first 18 to 24 hours. You should see him start nursing within two hours of birth. This will provide him with all the nutrition he needs but should the dam die, is in distress, or is having other problems nursing her young, you must have bottles with spare nipples and nutrition on hand.

A mother in good health will produce colostrum, a yellowish thick milk which gives the cria's immune system a kick-start and provides it with antibodies not passed to it during the pregnancy. The cria's body has a unique design; its intestines can absorb these antibodies into its bloodstream, but this can only happen for the first 12 to 18 hours after birth. This gives your cria the very best start at a healthy life because those antibodies are specific to your llama's surroundings and herd.

If your cria does not nurse within a couple of hours or you are concerned that he isn't nursing sufficiently, you can provide a colostrum supplement, but you must do it quickly. Feed the supplement every 3 to 4 hours using a bottle and continue for up to 48 hours after the birth – follow the package instructions carefully.

After the first 48 hours, if your cria still isn't nursing properly, swap the colostrum supplement for a milk replacement. Make sure it is at least 24% protein. This will ensure he continues to receive the right nutrition to grow and develop properly. Try not to handle the cria too much while you are feeding – this will minimize the potential for behavioral issues.

The process of the birth exposes the cria to lots of microorganisms and pathogens that can lead to digestive distress; this can lead to diarrhea and dehydration. Whether the dam is feeding her young or you are, you must supplement with electrolytes. Be sure you provide the electrolytes in a separate feeding from milk products.

Chapter 9: Training Your Llama

Quick Fact — *Llamas are one of the smartest and easiest animals to train but patience is required. They have long been used for guarding other animals, like flocks of sheep and sometimes alpaca herds and require little training to be effective at guarding an area or other animals.*

Training cats and dogs is relatively easy and some of us have done it often. We efficiently train them to do the basics, the things we want or need them to do, and stop them from doing things we don't want them to do.

Few llama and alpaca owners know the possibility of training their pets. Many owners ask if it's possible to train their llamas by themselves. The simple answer to this is yes. Be able to teach one by yourself if you have plenty of free time and patience. You'll have to learn llama and alpaca body language, understand normal and abnormal behavior and then follow the tips and tricks below to train them.

Note that if you are the type of person that gets nervous around animals, you may find it challenging to train them yourself, and "do-it-yourself" training is definitely not for people with a short fuse.

If you get frustrated by the aggressive or sluggish behavior of animals, you shouldn't try training one yourself. Even though llamas or alpacas are trainable, only a particular type of temperament can successfully do it; otherwise, you may do more harm to the animal than good.

Many llama farmers try to train their creatures incorrectly and then become angry with the llamas when it doesn't work. Instead of changing their approach to training, they keep trying the same things repeatedly. Ultimately, they give up and conclude it's impossible.

Most llama farmers are of the belief that it's impossible to train llamas by themselves are those who have tried and failed at it. The important thing to remember when training a llama is that when it isn't working, stop. Please consider what you are doing wrong. It isn't the llama's or alpaca's fault. And just like when training a dog, you should never end a session on a low note–the animal will remember and will associate training as unpleasant and be even less cooperative.

You'll need to understand how to re-educate these llamas. Essentially, you must learn to train a broken llama. The llama has equated humans with suffering and pain, and to get it back on track requires re-education. That's why it best you don't try to train them before you learn how to do it properly.

This chapter will take you through basic knowledge about training llamas.

So, let's get started.

What You Should Teach Your Llamas or Alpacas

Many people believe dogs are fast learners, and probably the quickest learners of all pets. But, when you compare llamas to dogs, it might interest you to know that llamas will learn more rapidly than dogs that walking without a leash is the best. Your focus should be to get them to walk by your side without a leash.

There are three categories of llama-training. You decide the level you want to take your llamas or alpacas to; in this respect, your decision depends on the reason you keep your herd.

If your goal for keeping a llama herd is simply for llama wool, then you may only need to teach them the basics to make the shearing process easy. If your llama will be a pack animal and has to follow you into the mountains, you must conduct lessons geared towards carrying a pack.

You can also train them to drive carts, obey commands such as sit down or get up, and much more. You decide what you want them to know and train them accordingly.

Let's look at the levels of llamas training and lessons under each group.

- **Basic School**

At this level, you teach them what constitutes "socially acceptable behavior."

For example, the law demands that any llama *not* on your property be kept under physical control via a lead and halter. This law implies that you must train each llama to be willing enough to take on a halter. Each llama or alpaca must also understand the basic concept of leading. This is non-negotiable training every llama must have.

Their physical needs demand you groom them, trim their nails, and inspect their body for any medical conditions. The implication is that you must train them to be calm enough for you to carry out these activities. They must know how – and be willing to – stand when tied, stand still without restraint, and lift their feet when asked to.

These are the essential schooling requirements for any llama or alpaca training. However, you can also take the practice to a more advanced level, which we explain next.

• Elementary School

At this level, you train them on specific skills that make for an enjoyable human-animal companion. Taking them through elementary school lessons is not only enjoyable for the llamas but also for you, as the handler.

Llamas and alpacas enjoy regular walks, so you need to train them to avoid trauma and trouble during these periodic excursions. Each llama must understand simple navigation concepts, such as the proper protocol to negotiate through gates. It should be able to follow behind on a narrow trail and understand how to respond in traffic.

Not only that, but you must also train each llama or alpaca on crossing vehicle and pedestrian bridges. They should even know how to negotiate mud, close trees, bush, shallow water and jump over low barriers such as falling logs, and human-made obstacles like ramps and steps.

Finally, when you need to load them into a vehicle, it can be a challenging game to play if you do not train them for such beforehand. You, therefore, must prepare them on how to load into vehicles readily.

They should also be trained on how to travel well in the sense they know how to take advantage of periodic "rest stops." Such training prevents them from soiling their traveling accommodation.

This level aims to train them to walk on a loose lead and rely on visual and verbal cues.

• Occupational Schooling

This level is for those willing to make their llama an enjoyable working partner. It will be best if you had more than the basic knowledge of llama training to get them to work for you. No llamas will naturally or willingly give themselves up for primary or elementary training.

However, performance llamas earn their keep by doing the following: packing, driving, and showing.

Packing refers to using llamas for loading and unloading. Such llama must be trained to stand untied anywhere, carry and maneuver loads around objects or obstacles, doing it alone by string or verbal direction.

Did you know llamas and alpacas can be trained to drive a cart? That's what driving means. It requires the use of distinct gaits and verbal commands like run, walk, jog, and ground drive commands like start, turn, and stop. Therefore, you must train the llama about these things and how to accept different types of llama-drawn vehicles, driving on roads, backing out of narrow spaces, etc.

Under this training level is housing llamas as pets. A pet llama must be trained to negotiate all types of in-house structures, obstacles, and restrictions such that you can easily find on the floor, in hallways, elevators, etc. It must know how to bring its head down for easier access and to be "spook proof."

• **High School**

Learning at this stage is the peak of llama training and this is where you train your llamas for show. If you want your llama to participate at a competitive level, you will need to prepare it to negotiate various obstacles defined by the show associations regulations.

Training Facilities and Safety

It's vital to consider where you are going to train your llama(s). The best place to do so is in a catch pen as it will willingly enter and can be held safe and secure.

If you are dealing with more than one llama and plan to train them all, you can't teach them together. You will need a small area for an individual llama as you start the beginner halter training. The training space shouldn't be too big, yet big enough to catch the llama and move it through the space safely.

Also, plan to have a double gate system that will allow you to maneuver the individual llama into the pen and secure the gate. Not only that, but the system also helps to create a small triangular-shaped pen with a smaller room. This design allows you to stay outside the pen but still handle the llama if needed.

Keep all the leads and halters within your reach. That way, you can access what you need for that session with ease without needing to leave the llama you are training. The llamas will also become used to seeing the leads and halter whenever they come into the barn.

Training Equipment

Though you need little equipment to get them through elementary school, you need to be sure you have the correct equipment to hand for the training session.

It is best to have a halter that fits and a good rope to serve as the lead. Other items include a stick to help guide the llama where you want it to go, a bag to carry a small portion of reward feed, etc.

It is useful to have these items at hand, but they are not essential. You could spend a fortune on them if you wanted to. However, if you must pay for a stick, you will have the same results using a PVC pipe or a pure bamboo cane, and you can use a cheap self-made bag to hold feed.

Just know that what matters most is the quality of the *training*, not how much you spend on equipment.

Trainer and Llama Safety

More important than training is the safety of both the llama and you. When preparing the facilities and equipment for training, ensure there are no sharp edges from which you or the llamas can get injured and no items around the training ground in which you or the llama can get entangled.

A good healthy llama is a powerful animal that delivers a quick and painful sidekick. Therefore, remember that whenever you are in the pen, do not stay in a compromising position where you can get kicked.

Remember that whenever a sidekick happens, it's most likely your fault and not that of the llama. A llama will naturally react when you touch it in an uncomfortable or unexpected place. Therefore, if you are unlucky enough to be side-kicked, note where you touched it animal – and learn from the experience.

Llamas and alpacas are good jumpers, especially when spooked. Be alert and do not lose concentration whenever you are around them. Anytime a llama jumps out of the pen, you need not fret; bring it back in, calm it down, and start again. Still, evaluate what you did that made the llama spook and jump away.

Bond of Trust

Every animal has the instinct to preserve themselves. While a dog will bite to defend itself and a cat will use its claws, a llama will run away as a form of protection.

Llamas and alpacas will do anything possible to protect themselves from danger; therefore, room to room is their friend. They will also do anything to protect their area. Their body language usually conveys the message, "This is my space, and I don't want you here. If you try to get into my space, I will either spit on you or run away."

You can use this knowledge to your advantage as a trainer; to earn a llama's trust enough to allow you into its space, you must be meticulous. Start by going into the pen the first couple of days to feed it, change its water, and clean its environment. Don't pay attention to it and don't try to corner it.

The idea is to let the llama know you are not a threat. That way it can be comfortable with you around.

The next step is to talk to the llama and move close to it slowly. If you move close and it wants to run away, don't stop it. Let it move. After a few days, you can take a PVC pipe or a sorting pole into the pen. Use it to rub its back gently. The llama will probably move; let it run but keep in contact with the pole and be careful not to corner it.

Continue to do this until you no longer need to use the pole to touch its back. Over time, it will discover that the rod is not a threat. When that happens, you can come close and touch its back with your hands.

Do undertake the process gently. Remember, you read earlier that "a llama will naturally react when you touch it in an uncomfortable or unexpected place." Therefore, touch from the shoulder, work your way to its neck, around its head, and under its belly.

Talk to your llama quietly while you do the touching. When it remains still while standing, walk out of the pen. Don't leave until it is standing quietly, which means you may have to back off and ignore it until the llama feels comfortable. Continue until it lets you touch the entire body, including the head. Then introduce it to a halter.

Rub the llama's neck and around its head, then gently put the halter on it. Remove it and put it on again. Repeat several times till you determine that the llama is comfortable with the process.

Don't make the mistake of starting halter-training the first time you put it on the llama. If you do, you will make the llama think the halter is a restraint and count it as an enemy. Your aim should be to make training a fun thing so the llama willingly goes for a walk with it on.

Tips to Train Llamas Successfully

The things you've been reading may sound easy to do, but that's only if you do it the right way. Here are tips you need to train your llamas or alpacas yourself, successfully:

• Be patient and don't rush the training

Here is the golden rule to training any llama or alpaca. You can easily get tempted to rush things when you start to make progress but that is a big mistake.

Also, know that llamas have different personalities. When you're training more than one llama, some will learn fast, while others will be slow to learn - have some patience with the slower ones.

• Repetition is key

Any llama will naturally resist training, and they won't get it at the first attempt. It is your duty as the trainer to get the llama comfortable doing whatever you want or need them to do.

Be it haltering, leading, brushing, desensitizing, fitting a pack, trekking, etc., they won't be comfortable with it on the first attempt. You must repeat the process until the llamas are happy about it.

Other things to consider include:

- Keeping the session short and simple
- Devote the right quantity of time
- Never get angry in front of your llama or alpaca
- Recognize failure and know when to withdraw
- Reward llamas when you make progress

All these constitute the attributes of a good llama or alpaca trainer. If you have trained them yourself, then you must learn to implement these attributes.

One reason you should train them is because a trained llama will earn you more on the market. Do you want to make money from keeping llamas? Check out the next chapter on tips for running a llama business.

Chapter 10: 10 Tips for Your Llama or Alpaca Business

Starting a business can be difficult for any entrepreneur but, it shouldn't be for you. If you follow this step-by-step journey, you can get started on your llama or alpaca business quickly. And even to raise them for the fun of it, you can still learn a thing or two.

10 Tips for Starting an Alpacas and Llamas Business

These tips will help you set up business with no stress and enjoy the dividends quickly.

1. Learn about Alpacas and Llamas

As with any new business venture, lots of research needs to be done so you don't struggle at any point in your journey.

During your research, decide to raise alpacas, llamas, or both. It will help to learn about their differences, feeding patterns, when and how to shear them, the best location for your farm, etc.

There are so many mistakes that can be avoided if you do your homework!

2. Get Advice From a Mentor or the Competition

A mentor is experienced at raising llamas and will show you what they've learned, he or she is already in the llama business and can serve as a guide for you. And if your farms are far enough apart, they won't see you as a threat to their business.

A mentor may be of immense support, especially in the early stages of the business. They will tell you what to do and what pitfalls to avoid and they are the people you can always turn to if you encounter a problem.

The competition is someone who might not want you in. They have been in the business longer than you, are experienced and may even be located near to you.

As much as you might not like it, it would help to learn about the competition – what their strengths and weaknesses are, the services they offer, what makes them unique, etc.

Leverage their weaknesses and provide that service.

For example, if your competition does not offer washing and drying of fiber, include that in the services you offer.

3. License and Registration

Before starting any business, you must register it with the proper authorities; there is usually one where you live or close by. Be sure you understand the terms and conditions. It is highly recommended to obtain a membership in AOA (Alpacas Owners Association).

You might also require a business plan (or proposal) that shows your current and long-term plans.

It is essential to talk to a business or tax consultant to guide you through the process. If you plan to sell the fleece from the animals, you will require a license from the state.

4. Funding

Funding is crucial to the survival of any start-up. At the initial stage, a lot of costs are incurred - buying the land, fencing, getting supplies, seeing a vet, licensing and registration, etc., and a lack of funds can delay the process.

Money is also needed to pay for manual labor around the farm.

You could apply for a loan from the bank if personal funds are not sufficient. There are government grants that cater to the needs of alpaca farmers.

5. Get Property

If you already have land, skip this step. However, you must make sure that the land is fit for the alpacas and llamas to graze. If not, consider expanding or buying a larger plot of land. Alpacas and llamas are social animals and love company.

Raising 6-7 alpacas needs about one acre of land. The land should be filled with plenty of healthy grass for grazing.

6. Check that the Location is Safe

The location of the farm should be safe from wild animals, parasites, and poisonous grass.

Build a fence around the farm site to make sure that the llamas don't wander away. You also need to check that the grasses are right for the animals to eat.

Some plants are toxic to alpacas, such as oleander, tobacco, poppies and buckwheat. Rid your farm of those.

7. Build Shelter

Although the animals will stay outdoors for most of the day, you still need a barn to keep them safe during extreme conditions.

A barn can be a simple structure; it need not be elaborate. However, it should be capable of serving as a windbreak and keeping the animals safe.

8. Get Other Tools and Equipment

Besides a barn, you will need other equipment on your farm. These include tools and supplies required for practical work including gloves, boots, hay-elevators, toe-trimming and teeth-cutting equipment, and shearing tools.

It is crucial to shear the animals once a year. If the animals are not sheared on time, the fiber may get too tangled and difficult to remove.

If you don't want to shear them yourself, you can always pay someone to do it for you.

9. Employ the Services of a Vet

You will require the services of an experienced veterinarian to help you cater to the health challenges of the animals. As time goes on, you might be able to handle health issues and routine care yourself under the guidance of a vet.

The number one killer of alpacas is parasites. You must ensure they are tested and dewormed regularly.

10. Make Provision for Feeding

Alpacas need a highly nutritious diet; they should be fed a healthy green diet. If you need to buy hay, it should be fresh.

Old, dusty, or moldy hay will not be the right choice for your animals, even though it may be the cheaper option. Also provide mineral supplements besides their hay.

Other Managerial Skills Required for Business

If you have gone into the llama and alpaca business, you have made a smart choice. Several people are thriving in the trade, but this success is not without planning and organization.

If you want your business to be lucrative, you must take strategic steps to make sure your progress is successful. In this section, we will introduce you to some tips you need to be abreast of. If you set your budget right and use the right managerial skills, you will succeed in this specialized business.

Budget and Management Tips

There is money involved in all businesses – llamas and alpacas inclusive. With the right budget and management guide, you are good to go. We have explained some areas you must check.

Your budget is the amount of capital you have envisioned to spend on your business, at least as a startup. Approach budgeting from the perspective of what your startup costs will be - consider the size of your business and how much money will be required to make it work.

First, consider how much money you can afford to put into the business and make sure your budget covers every area, including the following:

• Starting Up

Here, you must consider how much money it will cost you to purchase the first set of llamas and alpacas.

How many llamas and alpacas are you buying to get started? Take note that the number of animals you have determine how many crias will be born. It will also determine the amount of fleece.

When planning your budget, allocate a decent amount for necessities. While you are not trying to go beyond what you can afford, get the number of animals that best meets your business needs.

The number of llamas and alpacas you have determines the size of your ranch or farm. Consider the amount of hay you need to buy if you do not plan to engage in outdoor grazing. These items take space and money.

• Location

Also consider the best location for your llamas and alpacas. You will spend some amount of money on your ranch or farm, and its structure and organization will determine how well you can run the place. The movement and arrangement of animals is an important consideration.

The essential factors to be considered involve the number of animals you intend to have. Do you have enough grazing land or are you intending to feed your animals hay daily?

What will be the style and construction of your farm? Do you want to fence it permanently or create removable demarcations? Remember, you must have sections for cria birthing. Or do you plan to use a part of your barn?

If you have a robust budget, you may want to dig a well or provide a tap at your location. If otherwise, considering proximity to the source of water when creating your farm is wise.

If you plan to supplement their feed with pellets or grains, you need space for keeping large storage bins. In designing the management of your farm, give this factor ample consideration.

You must shear them yearly. Do you propose to do them on your ranch or elsewhere? If on your ranch, make room for it.

Fleece processing is another area that will influence your choice of location. Do you plan to process the fleece yourself? If yes, do you have enough space to accommodate the processes? Know that you must wash, dry, dye, and package it all.

You may need to perform other activities depending on what you want, so make sure you have sufficient space for whatever you need.

You may decide not to process the fiber yourself, so your budget must cover the processing cost. Remember that it is an expense you must make each time you shear them, mostly yearly.

The amount you allocate to location depends on the answers to these questions; take care to consider each area carefully.

• **Feeding**

This factor is crucial when budgeting for your business. How do you plan to feed your herd? You could provide them with hay every day. If this is your plan, have you factored the additional expense into your budget?

A viable plan is to locate a way of getting it at a relatively lower cost; is there a co-op close by? Could you barter some of your services in exchange?

Another option is to have a grazing area. If you provide for pasture, then you should have a tangible plan on how to manage areas in terms of irrigation, weeding, fertilization, etc.

Aside from pastures and hay, they will need supplements. These are essential for keeping their mineral and vitamin qualities in balance. Feed your animals pellets or grains.

What is your plan in this regard? Some people buy in bags and replenish as the need arises, while others buy it in bulk because it is cheaper. It saves time in going to buy often and some money.

Bulk-buying poses the question of storage. Large bins will be needed for storing the feed, and your budget should accommodate this expense.

Your herd will also drink water. Can you fetch water daily? If no, then will you have a well or tap close by?

• **Electricity**

You must have electricity on your farm. With the change of weather, you will need to warm the llama barn when it is cold (think of winter). If the weather is warm and they need to keep cool, you will need a fan to do the job.

Your source of water might also use electricity. When winter, and you have freezing waters, your water tank must be kept flowing.

If your dam delivers a cria and its temperature demands assistance, electricity will be vital then.

• **Manure**

Manure management is an important area to consider. They will produce manure every day and their living areas must be kept clean of it. A tangible plan on how to get the waste out is vital.

- **Trailer and Equipment**

Effective management of your farm depends on the availability of the essential equipment. Your budget should cover tools and the vital equipment you need to run your business successfully. Equipment like manure spreaders, elevators, UTVs, tractors, and so on is crucial.

You also need a trailer for easy mobility and a vehicle to transport them to veterinary checkups.

When going for AOA show and games, you will require a vehicle to tow your trailer. The distance you travel and the number of animals you transport at a time will determine the size of the vehicle.

- **Insurance**

Consider getting your farm and animals insured against liability. You can insure your llamas and alpacas against mortality and theft, and, on average, the cost of insurance is valued at 4.25% of the llama's value.

- **Miscellaneous**

There should be room for any unforeseen expenses that may come up, particularly emergencies.

Overall, you need a business plan to ensure the success of your business and a good plan will help your budget.

Writing Your Business Plan

Management begins with a business plan and coming up with one requires excellent management skills. This is a blueprint for your business and while it will take some thought to come up with one, it will guide you on the right steps to take and what to do.

Without a business plan, there are larger chances of failing in business. Proper planning will make sure you make the right choices and avoid mistakes. A business plan is essential for a newbie and even seasoned businessmen and women.

A business plan will help you determine the capital you put into the business, and also help you structure your budget properly to accommodate the necessities.

There are essentials for a business plan:

1. Analysis/Description

You must analyze your business and what it entails. It shows what you do, what you bring to the table, and your target market and is a pointer to your future activities.

2. Mission Statement

You state why you have a farm and where you are going with it. Your mission statement details your future goals and where you are aiming to be in, say 5- or 10-years' time.

3. Competitors

Your competitors are the farmers in the same business as you, including local and national farms. If you know about your competitors and how they operate in the market, you can make strategic moves to boost your brand and excel.

4. Market Opportunities and Threats

You must know how the market works and what is going on at any given time. Information is the key to opportunities here. Know what others are doing and how to do it better.

Market threats are factors that can hinder your business. These factors include your environment, the economy, resources, authorities, competitors, and so on and knowing what can pose a threat and how to deal with them will be of great help.

5. Income Sources and Goals

State the channels and strategies for earning your income. You can earn through llama and alpaca sales, sports, events, fiber sales and processing, and other side activities.

Your income goals refer to the amount you envision making from your llama and alpaca business and you can set weekly, monthly and yearly plans. Doing this will keep you focused on your priorities and strategize on how to hit the mark.

6. Expenses

You should have an idea of your business expenses. The crucial costs include the cost of starting up and maintaining your farm. Routine and eventual medical checkups and farm activities like shearing and processing must also be accounted for.

7. Marketing and Advertisement

This section includes how you envision promoting your sales. You could go down the traditional means of advertising, such as adverts in newspapers, magazines, and other prints, and you can also use the radio and television.

In the today's world, almost everything is online, and you should have a website for your business to ensure it is visible to the world. If you have your target market outside of your locale, then make your website all-encompassing.

Use several languages and offer translation in different languages. Social media platforms are also a viable means of advertisement; Twitter, Facebook, Instagram and other media are popular platforms for businesses.

A Facebook business page is another way of having a virtual office. Word of mouth has always been a viable option, and businesses thrive on referrals. Recommendations are good for business awareness and growth.

Explore clubs, shows and events that promote llama and alpaca sales.

The price tag attached to these areas differs according to the geographical location. Your taste also determines how much you spend; if you want a top-notch construction be ready to spend a LOT, or consider a lower-priced but functional structure.

8. Milestones

These are significant events that drive your business so indicate the ones you want to achieve to boost your business quickly. Any activity geared towards building your business should be part of your plan.

In this section, your plan should cover activities like llama and alpaca herd acquisition, building a website, fencing, constructing barns, etc.

More Tips on Management

A successful business hinges on successful day-to-day management. With adequate management, your business will cross borders. Areas to note are:

• Accounting

The accounts department is vital to any business and keeping income and expenditure records is essential. These will show you if you are making money or where you are spending more than necessary.

Since you are just getting started, you need to spend less and save more. With time, you can hire an accountant or bookkeeper, but meanwhile, several applications can aid you here. Most people use WAVE accounting, QuickBooks, FreshBooks, or something similar but reputable.

• Associations

Belonging to a relevant association is essential to business growth. It is an opportunity to network and meet people in the trade, and you can also learn from people who have been into the llama and alpaca business for some time.

There are several associations to join, like the Alpacas Owners Association, Inc. (AOA). Get licensed and identify with the association and observe local and national ordinances and regulations on owning a llama and alpaca business.

- **Tax**

You will need to pay tax and you can prepare your taxes yourself or have someone to do it for you, but you must consider the cost if you choose the latter.

- **Labor/Help**

For the smooth running of your business, you may have to hire help. If you cannot afford permanent staff at the initial stage of the business, hire temporary help.

- **Marketing**

Spreading the news about your business and increasing traffic is essential for business growth. Manage your website and social media handles yourself or hire a marketer or someone who is social media savvy.

- **Repairs**

Have the money to repair all broken equipment, taps and water lines, fencing, etc. to run your business without stress.

Areas Where You Can Make Money

There are several areas you can generate an income, including:

- **Sales**

The first thing that comes to your mind when going into llama and alpaca business is the prospect of selling them for money. You can also go into breeding and sell the crias.

- **Manure**

They will produce manure every day. What will you do with it? You can use it on your field or pasture as practical sources of fertilizer or sell it on to other farmers.

This source is a dual advantage for you. You get to make money by keeping your animals' living areas clean. It may interest you to know that llama poop is virtually odorless and is commonly known as "llama beans". It is one of the best fertilizers, completely natural and eco-friendly. Historically, dried llama poop was burned by the Peruvian Incas as a form of fuel.

- **Fiber**

You must shear them yearly. It not only benefits them health-wise, but it also yields money, and some people prefer buying raw fiber while others prefer to buy it processed.

While you may choose to process the fleece, be aware that washing, drying, dyeing, up to the point of delivery, may be hectic and with every stage comes financial commitment. However, every bit of money you put into processing the fleece will yield you more profit.

The yarn produced by processing llama fiber is lightweight and soft. It is also very warm, which is why the softer undercoat is used to produce handicrafts and garments. The coarser undercoat is typically used to make rope and rugs.

- **Events and Shows**

You can make money from your llamas and alpacas by taking them to animal shows and events where they participate in sports and work.

Strategies to Prosper in the Alpaca and Llama Business

There are strategies you can use to excel in your business, including:

- **Get Information**

Ask people questions about everything. Learn more on top of what you know already because you can never have too much information. Always seek to understand why, how, what, and where.

- **Take Notes and Pictures**

You may have a unique arrangement in mind, but you can learn from others. Visit other farms and take notes and pictures. Add ideas from other businesses to create a unique and comprehensive style.

- **Work in Conformity with your Local Authorities**

Check with your local authorities to learn what is allowed and what is not. If you have chosen a site to locate them, make sure that it is authorized.

- **Customers Feedback**

Encourage customers' feedback. Your business will grow if you please the market and satisfaction, quality, and consistency are essential to business growth.

Mistakes to Avoid in Business

Anyone new to any business may make mistakes. It is why a guide is necessary. If you know the paths to avoid, you will not have to walk them, at least not consciously. Some mistakes to avoid are:

- **Unsafe Purchase**

There are many people out there looking to sell their animals. Being a newbie in the business, you may want to jump at the cheapest sale you can find, but sometimes these purchases may turn out not to be beneficial.

It is safer to buy your animals from the general market. If you are buying from an individual, endeavor to scrutinize the animal to decipher its health status. Do not buy animals that look malnourished and sick. Enlist the services of a veterinarian to be on the safe side.

- **Negligence of Health Care**

Mother Nature will play a massive role in the birth and growth of your cria. However, you should not mistakenly leave them entirely alone. If you do not have the time and amount of commitment needed to care for them, then you have no business owning them. It is that serious.

Get help. Many people looking to start their farms will be glad to get the experience while earning on the side.

• Overlooking The Authorities

The ordinances in your location bind you, and you must conform to these rules. If you locate your farm or have your animals grazing where they are not allowed to, you are violating the rules. The consequences of this action may be serious for your business.

Do not mistakenly violate the rules.

• Overlooking Necessities

When it involves money, you may be tempted to overlook it. Please do not. Do not forget necessities like repairs, purchases, replacements, etc.

Bonus Chapter – Llama Terminology

To succeed in your llama or alpaca business, there are several terms you must understand:

- **Alarm Call** – the sound male llamas make when they feel their herd is under threat. It sounds like a turkey call, an engine turning over or a combination thereof.

- **Artificial Insemination (AI)** – a process where semen is taken from a male and placed manually into the uterus or cervix of a female llama.

- **Banana Ears** – a term describing llama ears that curve inwards and look similar to the size and shape of a banana.

- **Berserk Male Syndrome** – a condition describing a male llama that imprints on humans the wrong way and, when reaching puberty, becomes aggressive towards humans. Once it starts, this behavior cannot be changed.

- **Body Score** – a value given based on how thin or fat an animal is. The values range from 1 to 9, where 1 is emaciated, 5 is optimal and 9 is obese.

- **Bone** - a term describing the size of the llama's skeletal frame - those with large frames are said to have "a lot of bone."

- **Colostrum** - the first milk a female llama produces around the time of birth, rich in antibodies that the cria needs in the first 24 hours after birth.

- **Concentrates** - a supplemental feed dense in energy and lower in fiber. This includes multiple types of grains that are combined into a feed.

- **Cria** - describes a llama from birth to weaning.

- **Dam** - a female llama that has given birth.

- **Dung Pile** - an area where llamas defecate and urinate - they usually decide the area for themselves and there may be several areas in a pasture or field.

- **Dust Pile** - an area where llamas roll.

- **Embryo Transfer (ET)** - where early embryos are taken from a female and transferred into another.

- **Forage** - a food component that is lower in energy and higher in fiber, including hay, legumes and grasses.

- **Gait** - locomotion or movement. Llama gaits include walk, trot, pace, gallop, and pronk.

- **Gallop** - three-beat gait where the four feet are never on the ground simultaneously - the fastest of all gaits.

- **Get of Sire** - a llama show class where three llamas with the same sire and two or more dams are shown in a group - the judge wants to see consistency in the sire's influence.

- **Going Down** - when the female is receptive to the male she will drop to a 'kushed' position, known as "going down" for the sire.

- **Herdsire** - a male llama on a llama farm used purely for breeding - also called a stud.

- **Humming** - a sound made by llamas when they are hot, stressed, tired, concerned, curious, uncomfortable or tired.

- **Knock-kneed** – a llama condition whereby the front knees are angled inwards, known medically as carpal valgus. The condition causes incorrect movement in the llama and can lead to degenerative disease in the joints. These llamas also 'wing' when walking – see below.

- **Kush** – a term describing a llama lying down and is also the command used to get a llama to lie down.

- **Lama** – the genus llamas and alpacas are classified in.

- **Maiden Female** – an unbred female, usually too young for breeding.

- **Open Female - a** female that isn't pregnant.

- **Over-conditioned** – the polite way to say that a llama is fat.

- **Pace** – a two-beat gait where the rear and front limbs on the same side move backward or forward simultaneously. A medium speed, it is the least stable.

- **Packer** – a llama that can carry large loads to travel over long distances, usually with a lighter wool cover and larger than an average llama.

- **Paddling** – a term describing faulty movement where the llama's front feet swing out from the body as the leg moves forward. Usually caused by the llama having too wide a chest, sometimes genetically, but more typically in overweight llamas with a lot of fat in their chests.

- **Produce of Dam** – a class in a llama show where a pair of llamas with the same dam but different sires are show together – the judge wants to see consistency in the dam's influence.

- **Preemie** – a premature cria.

- **Pronking** – a term describing a gait where a llama bounces stiff-legged into the air, usually when playing or escaping from predators.

- **Rolling** – an activity llama do a lot; they lie on their sides and roll several times, either completely over or halfway, They do it to keep their fibers open, creating air pockets that provide extra insulation.

- **Sickle-hocked** – a llama fault where the hind feet go forward too far, creating a sickle shape at the hind quarters when the llama is seen from the side.

- **Sire** – a male llama that has sired at least one cria.

- **Stud** – see Herdsire – a male llama used for breeding.

- **Three-in-one** – commonly used to describe a female llama, sold when pregnant and with a cria. Effectively, you are getting three llamas for the price of one – the dam, the unborn cria, and the unweaned cria.

- **Tipped ears** – a term that refers to llama ears not quite erect. This is caused by cartilage in the ear tips that isn't strong enough to stand and can be genetic, caused by frostbite or by prematurity. It is not considered a major llama fault.

- **Topline** – commonly used to describe a llama's back when seen from the side. The ideal topline is level from the withers to the tail.

- **Trot** – a two-beat gait where the diagonal rear and front limbs move backward or forward simultaneously. A medium speed, it is a stable gait.

- **Underconditioned** – used to describe an underweight llama.

- **Walk** – a four-beat gait where three feet maintain ground contact at any one time. It is the slowest of all gaits.

- **Weanling** – a llama of less than 12 months old - already weaned.

- **Winging - used** for describing faulty movement. When it moves one front foot forward, the front feet swing in and then away from the llama's body before being placed back on the ground. Typically, this is seen in knock-kneed llamas and is worse in those that are severely knock-kneed.

• **Woolies** – sometimes used to describe llamas with a very heavy wool coverage.

• **Yearling** – a llama between one and two years old.

Conclusion

Let's take a quick recap of all that you have learned from this book.

You learned why you should raise llamas or alpacas in the first chapter. In the second chapter, we explained the differences between llamas and alpacas, and now you should find it relatively easy to identify the breeds.

You should also know how to design facilities for them from our guidelines in the third chapter. Your first purchase of llamas and alpacas need not be a disaster because we have provided all the details you need to buy your first pair of same-sex llamas in the fourth chapter.

Spitting llamas should not be a strange phenomenon to you, as you now understood all the behavior and handling of these animals from the fifth chapter. You also learned what you can and cannot feed your llamas in the sixth chapter.

The seventh chapter covered what you need to know about the health, care, and prevention of diseases in llamas and alpacas. Birthing new life comes with its challenges in all animals, even humans. We have helped you understand the birthing process and how to care for the baby cria (baby llama).

You might not have realized that llamas can learn to do many things before you read this book, but now you know how to train your llamas or alpacas to do various, important tasks.

Are you ready to start your llama business now? Our last chapter provided tips that will help you ensure your business is a success.

This book is not one for you to read and forget. You can always refer to it while on your llama or alpaca journey.

You have a vital tool for raising llamas in your hands. Use it wisely!

Here's another book by Dion Rosser
that you might like

References

A guide to handling camelids. (2019, September 24). Veterinary-Practice.Com.

Alpaca Digestive System. (n.d.). Apple Mountain Alpacas. https://www.applemountainalpacas.com/mentoring/alpaca-digestive-system/

Alpacas and Llamas: What They Are & Why You Should Keep Them - Hobby Farms. (2016, August 8). Hobby Farms. https://www.hobbyfarms.com/alpacas-llamas-what-they-are-and-why-you-should-keep-them/

Alpacas as a Business. (2017, December 13). Alpacainfo.Com.

Breeds of Livestock - Llama — Breeds of Livestock, Department of Animal Science. (n.d.). Afs.Okstate. Edu. http://afs.okstate.edu/breeds/other/llama/

Carmen. (2013, June 20). *5 Important Reasons You Should Add Llamas To Your Livestock Herd - Off The Grid News.* Off the Grid News. https://www.offthegridnews.com/how-to-2/5-important-reasons-you-should-add-llamas-to-your-livestock-herd/

Dohner, J. (n.d.). *Selecting a Guard Llama*. Mother Earth News. https://www.motherearthnews.com/homesteading-and-livestock/selecting-a-guard-llama-zbcz1404

Herd Health of Llamas and Alpacas - Exotic and Laboratory Animals. (n.d.). Merck Veterinary Manual.

How to Buy A Llama? (n.d.). Www.Shagbarkridge.Com.

Labor and Delivery. (n.d.). The Alpaca Hacienda.

Llama Behavior. (n.d.). Fancycreekllamas.Com. http://fancycreekllamas.com/llama-care/15-llama-behavior

Llama Habits & Behavior. (n.d.).

Llama Housing & Fencing International Llama Association Educational Brochure #5. (n.d.).

Llama Shearing. (n.d.).

Llama Training: What You Should Teach Your Llamas. (2009). Llamas-Information.Com. http://www.llamas-information.com/llama-training/llama-training-what-you-should-teach-your-llamas/

Successful Business with Alpacas and Llamas. (n.d.).

Taylor, M. (2018, July 23). *You Can Actually Adopt a Llama or Alpaca as a Pet*. Good Housekeeping. https://www.goodhousekeeping.com/life/pets/a20706815/get-a-pet-llama/

Twitter, T., & LinkedIn, L. (n.d.). *A Guide to Llamas, Alpacas, Guanacos, and Vicuñas*. ThoughtCo.

CPSIA information can be obtained
at www.ICGtesting.com
Printed in the USA
LVHW091921180321
681865LV00001B/12